THE ULTIMATE RANGERS QUIZ BOOK

The *Ultimate* RANGERS Quiz Book

,000 QUESTIONS AND ANSWERS

David Mason

MAINSTREAM PUBLISHING

EDINBURGH AND LONDON

First published in Great Britain in 2001 by
MAINSTREAM PUBLISHING COMPANY (EDINBURGH) LTD
7 Albany Street
Edinburgh EH1 3UG

ISBN 1 84018 543 0

A catalogue record for this book is available from the British Library

Typeset in Stone
Printed and bound in Great Britain by
Cox and Wyman Ltd

CONTENTS

INTRODUCTION

The Rangers Ultimate Quiz Book is an authoritative compilation of queries from the official club historian, David Mason. It is packed full of questions (1000 in all) catering for every fan with an interest in the club and its history. Whether you are a young 'Teddy Bear' or an older enthusiast, the book is suited to just about every age with categories covering a wide spectrum. Simply dip into each section at random, or select your specialist subject.

It will broaden your knowledge of one of the most famous and illustrious football clubs in Europe and is the definitive compilation of questions about the club, its players and its achievements.

QUESTIONS

2001–02 SQUAD

1. From which side was Stefan Klos signed?

2. At Feyenoord, Bert Konterman was a teammate of which former Rangers star?

3. Who replaced Giovanni van Bronkhorst in the Rangers No 8 jersey?

4. Who was the stand-in captain to Barry Ferguson in season 2001–02?

5. What do Billy Dodds and Claudio Caniggia have in common?

6. Which English side did Peter Lovenkrands snub to sign for Rangers?

7. Who was the last Australian internationalist at Ibrox before Craig Moore?

8. Which former 1972 European Cup Winners' Cup hero returned to the Ibrox coaching staff in 2001?

9. What is the name of the new Rangers training facility in Milngavie?

10. What is the connection between Shota Arveladze and Jan Wouters?

11. Who replaced Jorg Albertz in the Rangers No 11 jersey?

12. Russell Latapy was an internationalist from which country?

13. Which of the Rangers 2001–02 squad was sent off during the 1998 World Cup finals?

14. Andrei Kanchelskis joined which English side on loan in season 2000–01?

15. Which Rangers player scored five goals against St Mirren in November 2000?

16. Russell Latapy scored his first competitive goal for Rangers against which side?

17. Which two Rangers stars have twins in football?

18. Who has the greatest number of Dutch caps, Frank

or Ronald de Boer?

19. Which side did Rangers open up their European campaign against in season 2000–01?

20. Which former Ibrox winger died in 2001?

21. Who started his career at Ibrox with two goals against Airdrie in a CIS Cup-tie?

22. What was Michael Mols' squad number in 2001–02?

23. How many of the Rangers squad in season 2001–02 had a 'v' in their surnames?

24. What do Tore Andre Flo and Billy Dodds have in common?

25. Which Rangers player was signed from Dutch side FC Breda?

1. When did Rangers first win the Scottish Cup, and who were their opponents?

2. Which side ended a famous tour of Britain with a highly entertaining match at Ibrox in 1945?

3. What 'hoodoo' was broken with a 4–0 win over Celtic in 1928?

4. When was the Ibrox 'Grandstand' opened?

5. What tragic event took place in the Old Firm fixture of 5 September 1931?

6. What was the first professional side to win nine successive League Championships?

7. Rangers 'won' the 1901 Glasgow Cup in unusual circumstances. What were they?

8. Why was the 1909 Scottish Cup withheld?

9. What is the significance of the date 2 January 1971?

10. Where did Rangers get the money that was used to build the 'New Ibrox' stadium in 1899?

11. From where does the name of the club derive?

12. Rangers lost their first-ever Scottish Cup final against which side?

13. From which club was Alex Ferguson signed?

14. Who were Rangers' first shirt sponsors?

15. Rangers shared the first Scottish League Championship with what club?

16. What was unusual about league season 1898–99?

17. In which season did Rangers dispense with their traditional V-neck jersey?

18. Who were the two Rangers players who competed in the 1978 World Cup in Argentina?

19. Who was the only Rangers player to make an appearance in the 1986 World Cup in Mexico?

20. Which striker scored Rangers' first-ever goal in European competition?

21. What is the significance of Blairgowrie in Rangers' history?

22. Who was in the Rangers goal in the 1–0 Scottish Cup defeat at Berwick in 1967?

23. Which English side 'opened' Old Ibrox Park in 1887?

24. In what season were substitutes first used in Scottish football: 1966–67, 1967–68 or 1968–69?

25. Who was the first Rangers player to be substituted: Jim Forrest, George McLean or Jimmy Millar?

IN THE PAST

1. When was the first penalty kick?
2. The Rangers Chairman between 1912 and 1923 was a relation of which TV sports presenter and former Scottish internationalist?
3. When did Scottish football adopt professionalism?
4. What was the third ground that Rangers called home?
5. When Rangers won the Scottish Cup in 1928, it ended a 'drought' of how long without the Cup?
6. Which famous statesman visited Ibrox in 1946?
7. When does the Loving Cup ceremony take place?
8. Who was manager when the Rangers Social Club was opened?

9. Rangers celebrated 100 years at Ibrox in 1999 in a scheduled league match against which side?

10. Up to and including Dick Advocaat, how many managers did not play for Rangers?

11. In the early years, how did they cut the grass on the playing field?

12. Only once did Rangers not wear their traditional blue jersey. What replaced it?

13. What was Rangers' worst league position?

14. Who was the first non-UK 'foreign' player to win a Scottish Cup medal for Rangers?

15. What was the significance of the 1920 Championship win to manager William Wilton?

16. What military service did William Struth and William Wilton perform during the First World War?

17. Who had to be excused from school to play for Rangers and scored the only goal in his debut against Arsenal?

18. Who was the great 'Iron Curtain' defender who later emigrated to Canada?

19. Who was the star of Scot Symon's side between 1956 and 1964 who resurrected his career after being shot in Korea while on active service with the Black Watch?

20. Who played under Scot Symon and Preston North End and was brought to Ibrox by the Rangers boss?

21. The transfer of Davie Wilson to Dundee United paved the way for whose transfer to Rangers?

22. What position did Rangers hold in the league when Scot Symon was sacked as manager?

23. Which club did Jim Baxter join when he left Rangers?

24. What was the first foreign side to visit Ibrox?

25. What was the second ground that Rangers called home after they left Fleshers Haugh?

CUP FINALS

1. Who provided the cross for Derek Johnstone when he became the youngest player to score in a major final, nodding the winner against Celtic in the League Cup final of 1970 at the tender age of 16?

2. Who were the other Rangers scorers when Tom Forsyth's goal gave the Ibrox side a 3–2 win over Celtic in the Centenary Scottish Cup final in 1973?

3. What '60s star scored his first goal for Rangers and helped the side to the Scottish Cup in the process?

4. Rangers won the first League Cup competition against which side?

5. Who captained Rangers in the 1970 League Cup final to give Willie Waddell his first success as the Light Blues' manager?

6. Who was the Rangers captain in the 1991 Premier

League Championship clincher against Aberdeen?

7. What was the aggregate scoreline in the 1961 European Cup Winners' Cup final against Fiorentina?

8. Who was the Rangers goalkeeper in the 1981 Scottish Cup final?

9. Which two Tannadice players won Scottish Cup medals in Dundee United's famous 1994 success over Rangers, then later joined the Ibrox side?

10. Maurice Johnston won his only Scottish Cup Winners' medal with what side?

11. What was Rangers' biggest defeat in a League Cup match?

12. The biggest margin of victory Rangers achieved in a League Cup final was against what side?

13. What was Rangers' biggest Scottish Cup final win over Celtic?

14. Who won Scottish Cup medals with Motherwell and Rangers?

15. Who was the only Rangers player to win Scottish Cup medals before and after the First World War?

16. Who was sent off against Rangers in a League Cup final, then later joined the Ibrox side?

17. Rangers reached the Scottish Cup final on eight successive occasions in the 1970s and '80s. How many did they win?

18. Who missed a penalty for Rangers in the 1961 European Cup Winners' Cup final?

19. A one-off tournament which replaced the Scottish Cup in 1946 was won by Rangers. What was it?

20. Which two players played in both the 1967 and 1972 European Cup Winners' Cup finals?

21. Who scored twice to give Rangers the Scottish Cup in a 2–0 victory over Kilmarnock in 1960?

22. Who was the youngest player afield in the 1962 Scottish Cup final, who went on to help Rangers to the Cup again in 1964 and 1966?

23. Three players won five Scottish Cup Winners' medals between 1971 and 1982. Who were they?

24. Derek Johnstone scored in just 42 seconds of the Scottish Cup final against Hearts in what year?

25. Who scored a hat-trick in the 'Laudrup final' of 1997?

EUROPE

1. Who were Rangers' opponents in their first European Cup Winners' Cup final in 1961?

2. Who were Rangers' first European opponents?

3. Which English team knocked Rangers out of the European Fairs Cities Cup in 1969?

4. What was unusual about Rangers' magnificent European Cup run of 1992–93?

5. Which Argentinian World Cup star scored for Valencia to put Rangers out of Europe in 1979?

6. Ally McCoist scored a hat-trick only once in Europe – against which side?

7. Andy Goram had an unhappy start to his European career at Ibrox against which side?

8. What was the sequence of scores in the 1972 European Cup Winners' Cup final, beginning with 1–0?

9. Who lost his place in the 1972 Barcelona final through a late injury?

10. Rangers star Paul Gascoigne was red-carded twice in Europe for Rangers. Against which sides?

11. Which Dutch club that faced Rangers in European competition in the '60s is no longer in existence?

12. Which European tournament did Rangers play in in the year following the European ban in 1973?

13. What was unusual about the jersey Rangers wore in France in their European Cup match with Auxerre in 1996?

14. In the mid-'90s Rangers had a disastrous week, losing to Falkirk in the League Cup and Celtic in the league, as well as losing to which side in Europe?

15. What was the first European side to face Rangers in competition during Souness' tenure?

16. Robert Russell scored a famous goal that helped Rangers to victory over Dutch champions PSV Eindhoven in 1978. Who scored the other Rangers goals?

17. Which was the first Italian side Rangers faced in European competition?

18. Which German side did Rangers defeat 8–0 in the European Cup Winners' Cup in 1960?

19. Who scored four goals in Rangers' European record 8–0 away victory against Valetta in the Cup Winners' Cup in 1984?

20. Which was the first English side that Rangers faced in European competition?

21. Who was the legendary German goalkeeper who faced Rangers in the 1972 European Cup Winners' Cup semi-final tie?

22. When Rangers defeated the Russian side Alania Vladikavkaz in 1996, what was the away scoreline?

23. Who scored Rangers' equaliser in the 2–2 draw with Marseilles at Ibrox in the 1993 European Cup campaign?

24. Which other German side did Rangers face on the way to the 1967 European Cup Winners' Cup final encounter with Bayern Munich?

25. Which Spanish side inflicted an early UEFA Cup defeat for Rangers in 1985?

CONTINENTAL FOOTBALL

1. Which team was first to beat Rangers at Ibrox in European competition?

2. Who was the first player with a European Cup Winners' medal to play for Rangers?

3. Who was the Polish star who tormented Rangers, then England, in the 1960s and helped ease Alf Ramsey's men out of the World Cup?

4. After Gornik put Rangers out of the European Cup Winners' Cup in 1969, they progressed in the tournament only to lose out to which English side in the final?

5. Which was the first Spanish side Rangers faced in European competition?

6. Which 60's star missed a European tie because he got caught in traffic?

7. Who was the young full-back whose Rangers career was upset in the defeat from Gornik in 1969, ultimately precipitating his departure from Ibrox?

8. What was the only major trophy that Terry Butcher won with Ipswich prior to joining Rangers?

9. What did Mark Hateley, Ray Wilkins and Brian Laudrup have in common?

10. What was Rangers' best unbeaten run in Europe?

11. Which was the first European side that John Greig faced as manager of Rangers?

12. Which was the first Irish side Rangers faced in European competition?

13. Which was the first Italian side Rangers defeated over two legs in European competition?

14. Which was the first English side Rangers defeated over two legs in European competition?

15. Rangers progressed in Europe on the toss of a coin against which side?

16. Which midfielder scored Rangers' only goals in Europe in season 1991–92 when the club exited to Sparta Prague?

17. Rangers lost out in the UEFA Cup first round to a side from Pamplona in Spain. Which?

18. Which German side defeated Rangers in the 1989 European Cup?

19. Who vowed he would never take another penalty after missing a spot-kick against Athletico Bilbao in 1969?

20. What was the basis of Dynamo Kiev's complaints to UEFA after they faced Rangers in 1987?

21. Which was the first German side Rangers faced in European competition?

22. Which side did Rangers defeat in Europe on the 'away goals' rule in 1972?

23. Which was the first Dutch side Rangers faced in European competition?

24. Rangers were taken to a replay twice in European competition before the 'away goals' rule came into force. Once was against Nice. Which was the other club?

25. What was the scoreline at Ibrox when Rangers were shaded out of the UEFA Cup in season 1984–85 by Inter Milan?

OLD FIRM

1. What was Rangers' biggest victory over Celtic?

2. Who was the last player before Maurice Johnston to cross the Old Firm divide?

3. How many goals did Maurice Johnston score for Rangers in games against Celtic?

4. Which former Celtic boss faced Rangers as a player in a European tie in 1984?

5. Which two sides played a testimonial for the Ibrox disaster?

6. Who won the Scottish Cup with Rangers and Celtic in modern times?

7. Who scored the winning goal in the 1986–87 League Cup win over Celtic?

8. In 18 matches for Rangers against Celtic between 1960 and 1965, Baxter was on the losing side how many times?

9. Which was the only father-and-son partnership to score against Celtic for Rangers?

10. Which of these players was never ordered off against Celtic: Alfie Conn, Alex MacDonald or Derek Johnstone?

11. In what year did both Sandy Jardine and Davie Cooper score wonder goals against Celtic in the Dryborough Cup final?

12. Who held the Rangers goalscoring record against Celtic before being overtaken by Ally McCoist?

13. In the famous 5–1 win over Celtic in 1988, who scored twice for Rangers?

14. Who scored for both Rangers and Celtic at Hampden in consecutive Old Firm fixtures in 1995?

15. Who was the top goalscorer in the 4–1 and 5–1 league victories Rangers inflicted on their Old Firm rivals in season 1988–89?

16. Who scored a double for the Light Blues when Rangers and Celtic fought out a 4–4 draw in the

League Championship in 1986?

17. What was the scoreline in the fateful match following which many died or were injured in the Ibrox Disaster?

18. Which former Celtic star assisted Walter Smith in a scouting role in the late-'90s?

19. Andy Goram saved a vital penalty against which Celtic star to help Rangers to the Championship in 1996?

20. Which defender signed for Rangers for £2 million in 1994 and made his debut at Hampden in a victory over Celtic?

21. In the Old Firm context, what did Ally McCoist and Nigel Spackman have in common?

22. Ally McCoist scored hat-tricks in two cup finals over Celtic. What were they?

23. Who was the unfortunate goalkeeper in Rangers' 7–1 League Cup defeat by Celtic in 1957?

24. In what year was the first Old Firm fixture?

25. John Greig played in how many Scottish Cup final wins over Celtic?

NICKNAMES

1. Who were M & B?

2. Which Rangers and Scotland defender was called 'Tiger' after the great legendary star Jock Shaw?

3. Which Rangers full-back of the '70s and '80s was known to his teammates as 'Squeaky'?

4. Who was known as 'Bud'?

5. Which Dutch star was christened 'Mowgli' by teammate Ian Ferguson?

6. Which former Rangers captain was known as 'Corky'?

7. Who is known as 'Ledge'?

8. Who was often called 'The Moody Blue'?

9. Two former Rangers stars were known as 'Bomber'.

Who were they?

10. Which Rangers manager was called 'the Beau Brummel of football'?

11. Who was the 'Tin Man'?

12. Who was 'Deedle'?

13. Who was the 'Wee Prime Minister'?

14. Who earned his nickname from an English music hall star?

15. What was Bobby Shearer's nickname?

16. Who was known as 'Dandy'?

17. Who was nicknamed 'Wan Fit'?

18. Which goalkeeper was known as 'The Quiet Man'?

19. What was Jim Bett's nickname?

20. Who was known to his teammates as 'Jasper'?

21. Who was known as 'Slim' in Walter Smith's era?

22. Which midfielder from the Wallace years was known as 'Paddy'?

23. Who was 'Jaws'?

24. What was Davie Cooper's nickname?

25. What famous star was known as 'Doddie'?

LEGENDS

1. Who was known as 'The Wee Blue Devil'?

2. Who was signed from St Mirren as a stop-gap defender immediately after a 7–1 defeat from Celtic?

3. How old was Derek Johnstone when he scored the winning goal in the 1970 League Cup final?

4. Which two sides did Jim Baxter play for in between his spells at Ibrox?

5. From which club was Brian Laudrup signed?

6. Richard Gough and Mo Johnston both played for what American side?

7. Which influential player was injured against Aberdeen on 17 November 1987, critically affecting Rangers' title challenge?

8. From which club was Maurice Johnston signed?

9. Who scored on his Old Firm debut in just 33 seconds?

10. What was recently voted Rangers' greatest goal?

11. Who was the first Rangers player to win the Scottish Football Sportswriters Player of the Year award?

12. Derek Johnstone returned to Ibrox in 1985 for a second stint at the club. He was signed from which club?

13. Barcelona hero Alex MacDonald was signed by which Rangers manager?

14. Jim Baxter broke his leg in a European Cup tie against which side?

15. Who did Willie Henderson replace in the Rangers and Scotland side when he was first introduced to the team?

16. Which Rangers player was appointed 'manager' of Scotland while still registered as a Rangers player?

17. How many trebles did John Greig win as a player?

18. Who won the most Scottish caps – Willie Henderson, Eric Caldow or Jim Baxter?

19. John Greig scored a vital goal in a '60s World Cup qualifier against which side?

20. Against which side was Rangers' testimonial match for John Greig played?

21. What relative of Brian Laudrup followed him into Scottish football?

22. To which English side was Willie Henderson transferred when he left Rangers?

23. What do Kevin Keegan and Jorg Albertz have in common?

24. Which three Rangers players are twice winners of the Scottish Sportswriters Player of the Year award?

25. Which Ibrox legend scored the goal that put Rangers out of the Scottish Cup in 1985?

IBROX GREATS

1. Which player scored a hat-trick against Rangers then later earned a testimonial for service to the club?

2. Which Rangers star was considered 'one of the best players in football' by Dutch legend Ruud Gullit?

3. Who was the first player to win the Scottish Sportswriters Player of the Year award on two occasions?

4. Who is the only player to have won the Scottish Sportswriters Player of the Year award with two different clubs?

5. How many Scottish Cup Winners' medals did Andy Goram win?

6. In recent times, which two Rangers players won Scottish Cup Winners' medals with two different sides in successive seasons?

7. Who scored in every round of the Scottish Cup in season 1977–78?

8. Which Ibrox legend from the post-war era had a degree in Civil Engineering?

9. Who is the only Rangers player to have scored in three successive Scottish Cup finals?

10. Which manager gave Colin Jackson his Rangers first-team debut?

11. Which manager gave Ian Durrant his Rangers first-team debut?

12. Which manager gave Ally McCoist his Rangers first-team debut?

13. Which Rangers legend served in the armed forces in the Second World War and won the Military Medal?

14. Who made his debut with a hat-trick against his home-town team of Falkirk in 1955?

15. Which side provided the opposition in Richard Gough's testimonial match?

16. Which side provided the opposition in Colin Jackson's testimonial match?

17. In what year did Davie Cooper tragically die?

18. In what year did Brian Laudrup help Denmark to the European Championship?

19. Which Rangers No 1 was known as 'The Prince of Goalkeepers'?

20. Who was known simply as 'The Goalie'?

21. Which Ibrox legend won a Scottish Cup medal with Airdrie at the age of 18?

22. Who was the Rangers goalkeeper in the famous 1945 clash with Dynamo Moscow?

23. Which Rangers star scored the first Premier League hat-trick?

24. Who won a French Championship medal and five other titles with Rangers?

25. Which Rangers legend was appointed Dundee boss in 1954?

1. Davie Wilson, the '60s hero, scored six goals in a league match against which side?

2. Which legendary defender saw his career ended by a *sine die* suspension imposed by the SFA?

3. Who made his Rangers debut after the Berwick Rangers defeat in 1967 and went on to play almost 700 games for the club?

4. What was the transfer fee involved in the acquisition of Jim Baxter?

5. Who replaced Willie Waddell as a regular in the No 7 shirt?

6. Who was the penalty king who reputedly only missed three in his career?

7. Who scored the first-ever hat-trick by a Rangers

player in Europe?

8. Where did Mark Hateley begin his career?

9. Which Rangers captain was born in Stockholm?

10. Was Ian McMillan capped before he joined Rangers in 1958?

11. Who won most Scottish Cup medals, Jim Baxter or Willie Henderson?

12. Who was Rangers first £100,000 signing?

13. Who captained Rangers in the 1–0 defeat by Bayern Munich in 1967?

14. Who wore the No 6 jersey most often in the absence of Terry Butcher through season 1987–88, when he was out with a broken leg?

15. Which side did Rangers face in Tom Forsyth's testimonial in 1983?

16. Which former Rangers captain was born in Singapore?

17. Against which side did Colin Stein score a hat-trick on his Rangers debut?

18. Who joined Rangers in 1968 from St Johnstone for a fee of around £50,000?

19. Which legendary Rangers captain was signed from Hamilton for just £2,000 in 1955?

20. Which midfield player scored 19 goals in 41 starts in 1995–96?

21. Who won most Championship medals – Bob McPhail or Alan Morton?

22. From which club was Alan Morton signed?

23. How many goals did Jim Baxter score for Rangers – 24, 34 or 44?

24. Excluding championships, who won most major cups with Rangers – John Greig or Davie Cooper?

25. What did Bob McPhail, Willie Henderson and Ian McMillan have in common?

STADIUM

1. How many grounds have been home to Rangers throughout their history?

2. When was the first Ibrox Disaster?

3. To the nearest thousand, what is the Ibrox attendance record – 118,000, 126,000 or 139,000?

4. On what road is Ibrox Stadium situated?

5. Did Rangers introduce the place-name 'Ibrox' to Govan?

6. What are the four stands at Ibrox named?

7. Where were the cranes imported from during the construction of the top tier of the Main Stand?

8. What is written on the Rangers crest at the gables of the Main Stand?

9. The timber that was used to fit out the inner sanctums of the Main Stand in 1929 was originally destined for what famous cruise liner?

10. One trophy in the Ibrox Trophy Room was won by one of the founders, Moses McNeil, in 1876 for what?

11. What is written in blue and white tiles at the top of the façade of the Main Stand, above the main entrance?

12. What was unusual about the dressing-rooms when Rangers beat Aberdeen to clinch the 1991 Championship?

13. Where did Bill Struth grow tomatoes?

14. What came first – Ibrox Stadium or Copland Road Underground Station?

15. What was the original use of the Ibrox Trophy Room?

16. One of the mementoes in the Rangers Trophy Room, received from a European club, is a vase carved from solid coal, symbolising the industry of the country from which it came. Which country?

17. In what season did Ibrox become an all-ticket venue?

18. What change in football stadia construction was precipitated by the first Ibrox disaster?

19. What is the name of the 'baby bear' mascot at Ibrox?

20. What is the colour of the stone in the 'Marble Staircase'?

21. In what year did pop stars Billy Joel and Elton John play a gig at Ibrox?

22. What was the first of the modern stands built at Ibrox?

23. In what season did Rangers first beam back 'live' Premier League away matches to Ibrox?

24. Which English side officially 'opened' the Govan Stand in 1981?

25. When was the club-deck completed?

HITMEN

1. Who is the only player to score four goals for Rangers in a major cup final?

2. In what year did Mark Hateley retire as a Rangers player?

3. Which former Rangers striker scored five goals in a single match in the World Cup finals?

4. Which striker arrived at Ibrox in Davie White's record-breaking transfer deal?

5. Who was transferred to Brighton for £400,000?

6. Which of these never wore the No 9 jersey for Rangers – Ian Ferguson, Maurice Johnston or Ian Durrant?

7. Who did Jimmy Millar share the No 9 jersey with in the last few years of Scot Symon's tenure at Ibrox?

8. Which manager gave John MacDonald his Rangers first-team debut?

9. Which player has worn the No 9 jersey most often for Rangers in Scottish Cup finals?

10. Who scored more league goals for Rangers, Jim Forrest or Colin Stein?

11. Against which international side did Ally McCoist break his leg?

12. Which famous Hearts striker had a brother who played for Rangers?

13. In what year did Maurice Johnston miss a penalty for Celtic against Rangers?

14. Which Rangers keeper saved a penalty from Celtic's Maurice Johnston?

15. Who is the only other Rangers player apart from Ally McCoist to have won a European 'Golden Boot' award?

16. Who broke his leg in an off-the-field accident while on tour with Rangers in 1984?

17. Which two London clubs did Gordon Durie play with?

18. Who won most Scottish caps – Derek Parlane or Derek Johnstone?

19. Which great Rangers striker cost Rangers just £5,000 in a transfer from Dunfermline?

20. Which French striker had a short stint at Ibrox early in Dick Advocaat's career?

21. Which Rangers striker went on to win a League Cup medal with Raith Rovers?

22. Derek Johnstone was top goalscorer in Wallace's 1976 Treble side, but which young front man came next in the Rangers scoring charts?

23. Which prolific striker capitalised on the great wing play from Willie Waddell?

24. To which English side was Kevin Drinkell transferred?

25. Who took the No 9 jersey in season 1967–68 after the departure of Jim Forrest and George McLean?

1. Derek Johnstone and Derek Parlane headed the Rangers goalscoring charts in seven of the '70's ten seasons. Which other two players were the top goalscorers in the three remaining seasons?

2. When Willie Waddell led Rangers to the League Cup in 1970, it brought the first major trophy to the club in how long?

3. Who lifted the League Cup for the first time as captain in 1975?

4. How many trophies did Davie White win in his full managerial career?

5. The 1979 Scottish Cup final went to two replays against which side?

6. Which midfielder arrived from Hibs in exchange for Graham Fyfe and Ally Scott in 1976?

7. What was the first major domestic trophy that John Greig won as manager of Rangers?

8. Whose debut came in a Scottish Cup final under Willie Waddell?

9. Who scored the Rangers winner in the last minute of the 1978 League Cup final against Celtic?

10. Rangers were defeated 2–1 by Southampton in the final of what competition in season 1976–77?

11. What other major domestic trophies were in the Ibrox Trophy Room in the year Rangers had the European Cup Winners' Cup in their possession?

12. Who made a record called *Each Saturday* with Kenny Dalglish?

13. Which Rangers star of the Wallace 1978 Treble season played just two games under Graeme Souness?

14. Rangers lost home and away in the European Cup to which French side in 1975?

15. In the first of Wallace's 'Treble' seasons, which teams did Rangers face in the two major domestic cup finals?

16. After Rangers' glorious win over PSV Eindhoven in

the European Cup in 1978, the side lost out in the quarter-final to which German team?

17. Who was Rangers top goalscorer in season 1969–70?

18. Which legendary Rangers winger appeared as a substitute for Johan Cruyff in a Rest of Europe side against Benfica in 1970?

19. In the victorious European Cup Winners' Cup run of season 1971–72 against which side did Rangers kick off their European campaign?

20. Which '70s Rangers goalkeeper was signed from Stenhousemuir for £10,000?

21. Who was Rangers top goalscorer in John Greig's first season as boss in 1978–79?

22. Which Spanish side eliminated Rangers from the European Cup Winners' Cup in 1979?

23. Who was signed on loan from Manchester United in 1978 by John Greig?

24. Rangers participated in which British cup tournament in season 1974–75?

25. Rangers defeated which Swiss side in the European Cup Winners' Cup in 1977?

THE '80s

1. Which Rangers manager sold Ted McMinn?

2. Who scored the only goal in the 1984–85 League Cup final to give Jock Wallace his last trophy as Rangers boss?

3. Which manager gave Dave McPherson his Rangers first-team debut?

4. Which manager gave Scott Nisbet his Rangers first-team debut?

5. John Greig resigned after a defeat from which side at Ibrox?

6. Who briefly returned to Rangers on loan in time for the 1982 League Cup final?

7. Rangers beat Dundee United 4–1 in the 1981 Scottish Cup replay. What was the score in the first match?

8. When did Rangers last win a major trophy with an all-Scottish side?

9. Who was the only Rangers player to appear in the 1982 World Cup finals?

10. Which 19-year-old was nominated 'Man of the Match' in the 1986 League Cup win over Celtic?

11. Who was signed from West Ham in 1983 for a fee of £160,000?

12. Rangers were invited to play a testimonial match for former keeper Stewart Kennedy in 1985 by the side he played for at that time. What was the side?

13. Who was the Rangers skipper in the famous 4–1 Scottish Cup final victory over Dundee United in 1981?

14. Which legend played 104 consecutive first-class matches for Rangers between 1986 and 1988?

15. Three of the Dundee United side that faced Rangers on the way to the Championship in 1983 eventually found themselves at Ibrox. Who were they?

16. Which Aberdeen midfielder was signed for Rangers by Jock Wallace but found limited opportunities under Graeme Souness?

17. From which club was John McClelland signed?

18. Who signed Swedish internationalist Robert Prytz for Rangers?

19. From which club was Robert Prytz signed?

20. Who received a six-month suspension after being ordered off five times in a season in the '80s?

21. Which defender was signed for £225,000 from Hibernian in 1982?

22. Who was appointed John Greig's assistant manager in 1982?

23. When he left Rangers, which side did Jim Bett rejoin?

24. Which striker was signed by Jock Wallace for £100,000 from Clydebank in 1983?

25. Winger Ted McMinn was signed from which lowly Scottish side?

THE '90S

1. Which player was signed by Graeme Souness from Dunfermline in the early '90s?

2. True or false: Rangers had more players in the England squad for the 1990 World Cup than they had in Scotland's?

3. Which two Rangers players scored goals for Scotland in the 'Italia '90' World Cup finals?

4. Who was the only Rangers player to play in the 1998 World Cup for Scotland?

5. Jersey numbers one to six were used by the same players throughout the 1992 Scottish Cup Campaign. In order, name the players.

6. Who scored Rangers' first goal in the 2–1 Scottish Cup win over Aberdeen in 1993?

7. What was the venue of the 1993 Scottish Cup final?

8. Which Dundee United stars were signed by Rangers in a £750,000 transfer deal?

9 Who was involved in the switch that took Alan McLaren to Ibrox?

10. Who scored against every league side in season 1993–94?

11. Against which English side did Trevor Steven make his Rangers debut?

12. In whose testimonial match did Gary Stevens make his debut?

13. Whose testimonial caused a lockout at Ibrox when the gate exceeded expectations?

14. Which two Aberdeen players joined Rangers, one for just under £1 million and the other for £1.5 million?

15. Who was signed from Rosenborg in 1997 for a fee of around £2 million?

16. Where did Rangers clinch the 1990 League Championship?

17. In 1994, a crowd of over 20,000 turned up to see

which player score for the reserves in an Old Firm clash?

18. Who scored two late goals to give Rangers a 3–1 win over Celtic in the 1997 Ne'erday clash?

19. Who was introduced to the fans before a 1997 Old Firm match, then found his appearances for the Light Blues quite limited?

20. Which Rangers legend won the Scottish Professional Footballers Association Player of the Year award in 1992 after only his first season at Ibrox?

21. Who was signed on a free transfer as a late addition to the squad in 1996–97 as a replacement and cover for Andy Goram?

22. Who joined Rangers from Perugia for a fee of around £3.7 million?

23. Which keeper was signed from FC Copenhagen for a fee of £1.5 million?

24. Which Rangers No 11 scored 2 goals in the 1994 4–2 Ne'erday win over Celtic at Parkhead?

25. Which team did Rangers defeat 10–1 in the Scottish Cup in 1996?

CHAMPIONS LEAGUE

1. Who scored Rangers' only goal in the 1993 away tie against Marseilles?

2. Who wore the No 3 jersey in Rangers' exit to Levski Sofia in 1995?

3. Who wore the Rangers No 7 jersey in the 'Battle of Britain' win over Leeds United at Elland Road?

4. How many of the players who featured in the Rangers v Leeds 1993 Champions League tie were at Ibrox in Dick Advocaat's reign?

5. Who was the Marseilles goalkeeper Rangers faced in the Champions League in 1993?

6. In Rangers' 1992–93 European campaign, when they lost out to Marseilles in qualification, how many home games did the Ibrox side win?

7. Why was Rangers' match with CSKA Moscow played in Bochum, Germany in 1992?

8. Which Cypriot side did Rangers defeat on the way to the Champions League in 1995?

9. True or false: Rangers never won any of their Champions League matches in 1995–96?

10. Which German side did Rangers draw with home and away in the Champions League, with the match ending 2–2 on each occasion?

11. Which German striker scored for Marseilles at Ibrox in 1993?

12. Which Bulgarian side put Rangers out of the Champions Cup in 1993?

13. Who replaced Michael Mols when he was stretchered off in the Olympic Stadium, Munich in 1999?

14. During the group phase of the 1999–2000 Champions League, two Rangers players scored two goals each. Who were they?

15. Which team did Rangers defeat to progress to the group stages of the 1999–2000 Champions League?

16. Which former Ibrox star was in the squad list of one of Rangers opponents in the 1999–2000 Champions League group phase?

17. Which midfielder was drafted in by Dick Advocaat to fill a 'holding role' in blunting the strike threat from PSV Eindhoven at Ibrox in 1999?

18. True or false: Ruud van Nistelrooy scored for PSV against Rangers in the Champions League?

19. What was the significance of Michael Tarnat's goal in 1999?

20. What Dutch star made his European debut for Rangers quite emphatically in the 5–0 drubbing of Sturm Graz in 2000?

21. During the 1996–97 Champions League group phase, Richard Gough scored against Juventus and which other side?

22. Which Greek side came between Rangers and a place in the 1994–95 Champions League?

23. Which side inflicted Rangers' first defeat in the group stages of the Champions League?

24. Against which side did Rangers open the group phase of the 2000–2001 Champions League?

25. In the 2000–2001 competition, Rangers failed to progress after failing to record a win against which side in the final match of their group?

INTERNATIONAL CAPS

1. Which of these was never capped for Scotland – Alex Miller, Alex MacDonald or Tommy McLean?

2. Which three Rangers players were in the victorious Scotland side which defeated England 3–2 at Wembley in 1967?

3. Which Icelandic internationalist played with Rangers in the '60s?

4. Colin Stein scored four goals for Scotland against which country?

5. Which Rangers striker in the early '80s was an Australian international?

6. Who replaced Eric Caldow as full-back in the Scotland victory over England in 1967, when he was stretchered off with a broken leg?

7. Who served Rangers for 27 years, and won two Trebles and eight Scotland caps?

8. Which Rangers player's goal took Scotland to a play-off for the 1984 World Cup?

9. Which of these was never capped for Scotland – Alex MacDonald, John Brown or Bobby McKean?

10. Who won most caps – Billy Ritchie, Bobby Brown or Peter McCloy?

11. Who won most caps – Tom Forsyth or Derek Johnstone?

12. Who was the first Rangers player to score in the World Cup finals?

13. Who was the only Rangers player to regularly feature in the Scotland side in 1984?

14. Who became the second post-war Rangers player, after Billy Simpson, to play for Northern Ireland?

15. Which Rangers player holds the club record for Scottish international appearances?

16. Which Rangers player was one of the key figures in the Scots team dubbed the 'Wembley Wizards'?

17. One was capped, one wasn't. Which was which – Billy Ritchie and George Niven?

18. Rangers were represented in the 1974 World Cup by a player who served a country other than Scotland. Who was he?

19. Who won more Scottish caps – Davie Provan or Davie Robertson?

20. Who won more Scotland caps – Jimmy Millar or Ralph Brand?

21. Who won more caps for England – Gary Stevens or Trevor Steven?

22. Who scored the only goal in the 'Rous Cup' match between Scotland and England in 1985?

23. Which Rangers star earned 84 caps for England?

24. Who was the last Rangers player to score against England at Wembley?

25. Which three Rangers players were in the 1978 World Cup squad?

1. Which Aberdeen taxi driver was part of Rangers' victorious cup-winning side?

2. Which of the 1972 cup-winning side played in only three matches of the nine in the entire campaign?

3. Who was the top goalscorer in Rangers European Cup Winners' Cup campaign in 1971–72?

4. How many of the 1972 cup-winning side were born and raised in Glasgow?

5. How many of the 1972 European Cup Winners' Cup side went on to play in the English First Division?

6. What was the ban imposed on the club by UEFA immediately after the Barcelona final?

7. Whose leg break in an earlier round prevented his

appearance in the European Cup Winners' Cup final in Barcelona?

8. Which star of the Barcelona final received the Scottish Sportswriters Player of the Year award that season?

9. Apart from their appearance in the European Cup Winners' Cup, have Rangers played at the Nou Camp on any other occasion?

10. What was the official attendance at the Barcelona final – 35,000, 45,000 or 55,000?

11. When was Rangers' third goal in the final scored – at 49, 59 or 69 minutes?

12. Who wore the No 8 jersey in Barcelona?

13. The side that played in the final showed two changes from that which beat Bayern in the previous match. Who was drafted in to the team?

14. Which was the only team to beat Rangers in the European campaign that took them to Barcelona?

15. Which of the Barcelona side played fewest European matches in the run that season?

16. True or false: Peter McCloy was the only keeper used throughout the European campaign of 1971–72?

17. Who scored the goal in extra-time that gave Rangers an away goals win over Sporting Lisbon?

18. Who was signed from Motherwell for £40,000 just five months after the win in Barcelona?

19. Which German World Cup star played at full-back and grabbed the Bayern goal in the first leg of the semi-final in 1972?

20. Did Rangers play in European competition in the following season?

21. Which teams, apart from Dynamo Moscow, had Rangers faced in the European Cup Winners' Cup final before 1972?

22. In what year did Rangers first meet Dynamo Moscow?

23. Who wore the No 5 jersey in Barcelona?

24. One of Rangers' Barcelona heroes had to wait until 1981 before he represented the club again in Europe. Who was he?

25. Three of the Bayern side who lost out at the semi-final stage to Rangers were in the team that defeated the Ibrox men in the final five years earlier. All went on to win the World Cup with Germany in 1974. Who were they?

CLASSIC MATCHES

1. Who scored his first goal for Rangers to help the side to a Scottish Cup final victory in the '70s?

2. Who scored one of the most dramatic Old Firm goals on 7 January 1978 when he ran the full length of Ibrox, beginning and ending the move with a stunning goal while the Celtic players swarmed around the referee contesting an earlier penalty claim?

3. Why was Richard Gough's Old Firm debut more memorable than most?

4. Which players ended up in court after an Old Firm League fixture in 1987?

5. Which famous match took place on 24 May 1972?

6. What was the significance of Rangers' victory over Celtic on 16 March 1997, and what was the score?

7. Who were the scorers in Rangers' famous victory over Leeds United at Elland Road on 4 November 1992?

8. Who missed a last-minute penalty in the 1981 Scottish Cup final?

9. Who was sent off at Aberdeen in the penultimate league match in 1986–87?

10. Rangers won the Dubai Cup in 1987 by beating which side on penalties?

11. In what year did Jim Baxter score two goals in a famous Wembley victory for Scotland?

12. To what did Tory Gillick draw the referee's attention in the 1945 encounter against Dynamo Moscow?

13. Walter Smith saw his side complete the Treble against which side, and where?

14. Graeme Souness led Rangers to a 2–0 victory in his first Old Firm Ne'erday match as boss. McCoist got one of the goals, but who got the other?

15. A goal from whom and where clinched Jock Wallace's first Championship as Rangers manager?

16. Who scored Rangers' vital opening goal from the

penalty spot in the famous 1928 Scottish Cup final win over Celtic?

17. Who scored Rangers' equaliser from the penalty spot in the famous 2–2 draw with Dynamo Moscow in 1945?

18. Rangers defeated which side in two classic finals within the space of seven months in 1960?

19. In 1949, combined crowds of over 265,000 took in the Scottish Cup final and replay between Rangers and which side?

20. The 1964 Scottish Cup final is often named after the Dundee keeper who performed heroics in keeping out the Rangers forwards. Who was he?

21. Who was the Rangers No 9 on the day Kai Johansen's goal gave the Ibrox side a Scottish Cup replay win over Celtic in 1966?

22. At what position did Sandy Jardine play in the 1967 European Cup Winners' Cup final?

23. Rangers lost which influential player on the eve of the Scottish League Cup final in 1970, when Derek Johnstone nodded the only goal?

24. Who scored the Rangers goals in the dramatic 3–0

win at Celtic Park which effectively clinched the 1998–99 title?

25. Davie Cooper scored one of the greatest Rangers free-kick goals against Aberdeen in 1987 in what tournament?

ODD ONE OUT

1. Who is the odd one out – Graeme Roberts, Gordon Durie, Richard Gough, Trevor Steven or Alfie Conn?

2. Which of the following is odd man out – Reyna, Albertz or Konterman?

3. Which of the following won three Scottish Cup Winners' medals with Rangers – Russell, Dawson or Smith?

4. Which of the following never won an Old Firm cup final winners' medal – McMillan, Davis or Provan?

5. Which of the following won most Old Firm cup finals – Baxter, McKinnon or Henderson?

6. Which of these never won a Scottish Cup Winners' medal with Rangers – McClelland, Redford or Bett?

7. Which of these never topped the Rangers scoring charts in a season – John MacDonald, Gordon Smith or Sandy Clark?

8. Who received the fewest international caps – Colin Jackson, Stewart Kennedy or Derek Parlane?

9. Which of the following received the fewest international caps for Scotland – Colin Stein, Davie Cooper or Derek Johnstone?

10. Which of the following was not capped during his time with Rangers – Jim Stewart, Billy Ritchie or Bobby McKean?

11. Which of the following made the least number of Scottish Cup final appearances – Willie Johnston, Sandy Jardine or John Greig?

12. Who is the odd man out – Persson, Beck or Prytz?

13. Which of these is the odd one out – A.C. Milan, Juventus, Inter Milan or Fiorentina?

14. Which of these did not play for Rangers – Struth, Wilton, Symon, Waddell or Souness?

15. Which of these is the odd year out – 1964, 1976, 1993 or 1997?

16. How many of these never won a Treble – Struth, Wilton, Symon, Waddell, Wallace and Souness?

17. Two of these played for the same club. Who is the odd one out – Nerlinger, Laudrup or Numan?

18. Which of these is the odd one out in terms of service to Rangers – Baxter, W. Johnston, Stein, D. Johnstone or Jardine?

19. Which of these has never won a European medal – Flo, Numan, de Boer or Klos?

20. Which of the following have never faced Rangers in European competition – Red Star Belgrade, Dynamo Tbilisi or FC Zurich?

21. Which of these sides never won at Ibrox in Europe – Spurs, Cologne or Rapid Vienna?

22. Which of these sides have never beaten Rangers in the Premier League – Airdrie, Clydebank or Ayr United?

23. Who provided the best challenge to Rangers through the nine-in-a-row years – Celtic, Aberdeen or Hearts?

24. One of the following had a spell with Benfica – Thern, Petric, Prytz or Amato?

25. Which of the following sides did Maurice Johnston not play for – Partick Thistle, Falkirk, Nantes, Watford, Notts County or Everton?

GRAEME SOUNESS

1. With which London side did Graeme Souness begin his football career?

2. Rangers lost three times to which side in the Scottish Cup under Graeme Souness?

3. Which Turkish side did Graeme Souness go on to manage after leaving Ibrox?

4. Who scored the Light Blues' goal when Rangers lost their first league match under Souness at Easter Road?

5. How many appearances did Robert Russell make under Souness – 2, 4 or 6?

6. Which Danish defender had a short-lived career under Souness?

7. What was the last major trophy that Rangers won

under Graeme Souness?

8. With which player did Graeme Souness get entangled, leading to his dismissal at Easter Road in 1986?

9. What was Graeme Souness' last game as manager of Rangers?

10. Who was born in Cairo and signed by Souness from Maccabi?

11. From which side did Rangers sign Neale Cooper?

12. How many European Cup medals did Graeme Souness win?

13. Who was Graeme Souness' first signing?

14. Alex Ferguson dropped Graeme Souness for what World Cup match?

15. Hamilton Accies caused a major shock when they defeated Rangers in Souness' first attempt at the Scottish Cup, but which side upset the Ibrox side in the tournament in the following season?

16. Who scored the Hamilton Accies goal when the Lanarkshire side defeated Rangers in the Scottish Cup in Souness' first season as Ibrox boss?

17. Which Rangers player scored five times against Chris Woods?

18. Who was the Celtic goalkeeper when Rangers won 5–1 against their Old Firm rivals in 1989?

19. In what year did Graham Souness encourage the financial interest that David Murray took in Rangers?

20. Who was signed from Alloa, then went to Blackburn Rovers, but was a key member of Souness' side in between?

21. What did Graeme Souness call the 'worst day' of his playing career?

22. Who was the Berwick-born English internationalist who was signed by Graeme Souness in 1989?

23. Who was the former teammate and physio who joined Graeme Souness at Ibrox?

24. Against which side did Graeme Souness score his first league goal for Rangers?

25. The only jersey Terry Butcher wore throughout his time at Ibrox was the No 6 – true or false?

WALTER SMITH

1. Which Italian club did Sergio Porrini and Brian Laudrup play for?

2. Who is older, Barry Ferguson or Scott Wilson?

3. Who was the Norwegian defender signed by Walter Smith?

4. How many domestic titles did Paul Gascoigne win at other clubs before arriving at Rangers – zero, one or two?

5. Who scored and picked up a serious injury on his Rangers debut?

6. Which was the first European side Rangers faced in competition under Walter Smith?

7. Which Junior league side did Walter Smith play for?

8. Walter Smith enjoyed a short loan spell with which team during his term as a player with Dundee United?

9. Who was Smith's first major signing as manager of Rangers?

10. Walter Smith was assistant to which Scotland manager and when?

11. Excluding his Championship success, what was the first domestic trophy that Rangers won under Walter Smith and who provided the opposition?

12. Walter Smith led Rangers to a remarkable undefeated run in Europe, extending from 1991 to 1993. Over how many games were they undefeated?

13. Who was Smith's most expensive acquisition in his time at Ibrox?

14. What was Walter Smith's final domestic trophy as Rangers boss?

15. How many times did Walter Smith lead Rangers to a League Cup win?

16. Which teams did Rangers face in winning Scottish Cup finals during Walter Smith's reign as boss?

17. Rangers hit a record championship points total of 87

for 36 matches and trounced Hearts 5–1 in the Scottish Cup final in what season?

18. Rangers signed two players from Perugia in 1997. One was Marco Negri. Who was the other?

19. Through his Rangers career, Walter Smith led his side into 36 European Cup matches. How many did they win – 14, 16, or 18?

20. How many times did Rangers qualify for the group stages of the Champions League under Smith's leadership?

21. What was Walter Smith's last match as manager of Rangers?

22. What honour did Walter Smith receive from the Queen?

23. Which Rangers legend was Walter Smith's 'boyhood hero'?

24. In what year did Smith open the season with a challenge between what was called Rangers 'A' and Rangers 'B'?

25. Which was the last European side Rangers faced in competition under Walter Smith?

DICK ADVOCAAT

1. Which player did Rangers sign from a club that Dick Advocaat once played for?

2. When was Dick Advocaat born – 1945, 1947 or 1949?

3. For how long was Dick Advocaat manager of PSV Eindhoven?

4. How many times did PSV Eindhoven win the Dutch Championship under Advocaat?

5. Which World Cup tournament did Advocaat lead Holland into?

6. Which tournament did Rangers win first under Dick Advocaat and who were the opponents?

7. What was the first side that Rangers faced in European competition under Advocaat?

8. Which famous Dutch star was dismissed from the Holland side after a bust-up with Advocaat?

9. Who did Advocaat succeed as manager at PSV Eindhoven?

10. Jorg Albertz once played for his home-town team. Which team was it?

11. Which Dutch club did Ronald de Boer, Arthur Numan and Peter Huistra play for?

12. Which English side did Billy Dodds play for before his career took him to Ibrox?

13. What was the background to Advocaat's first visit to Ibrox?

14. Which American side did Dick Advocaat play for?

15. Which Dutch side did Rangers face in European competition that Advocaat later played for?

16. Who is taller, Kanchelskis, Klos or de Boer?

17. Where was Kenny Miller born?

18. Who is older, Arthur Numan or Michael Mols?

19. What was unique about the fans on cup-final day

in 2000?

20. Who put Rangers out of the UEFA Cup in Dick Advocaat's first season in charge of Rangers?

21. Which German side did Rangers oust from Europe in Advocaat's first season as Rangers boss?

22. From which club was Claudio Reyna signed?

23. Rangers almost achieved back-to-back Trebles for Advocaat, but lost out in the League Cup to which side?

24. How many points did Rangers win in the Champions League group stage of the 1999–2000 tournament?

25. What was the first team to beat Rangers at Ibrox in European competition under Dick Advocaat?

RECORD BREAKERS

1. Who is Rangers' all-time league goalscoring record holder – Ally McCoist, Bob McPhail or Jimmy Smith?

2. Who holds the Rangers record for league appearances, John Greig, Dougie Gray or Ally McCoist?

3. What was the record points margin when Rangers won the Championship in season 1999–2000?

4. Apart from Celtic, which three teams have the best Premier League record against Rangers?

5. A record crowd of around 65,000 watched a testimonial match at Ibrox for what player?

6. Who is the oldest player to represent Rangers in a Premier League match?

7. How many times did Rangers exceed 100 league goals in a season in the post-war era?

8. How many titles did Rangers win under Bill Struth?

9. How many goals did Ally McCoist score against Celtic in equalling Jimmy McGrory's record in Old Firm matches – 25, 27 or 29?

10. Who scored Rangers' fastest-recorded goal in April 1995 against Dundee United?

11. Who shares with Bob McPhail the Rangers record for most Scottish Cup Winners' medals?

12. After John Greig, who has had most Scottish Cup appearances?

13. A crowd of 104,679 broke the attendance record for a friendly in 1961. Who provided the opposition?

14. What is Rangers' record European victory?

15. The £17,500 fee that Rangers paid Raith Rovers for Jim Baxter was a Scottish record at the time – true or false?

16. Which Gers defender won 40 caps and played over 400 games without receiving a booking?

17. Which Rangers manager held the position for the shortest duration?

18. What was Rangers' lowest finish in the league?

19. Which Rangers player holds the record number of Scottish Cup final wins over Celtic?

20. Who was Rangers' longest-serving manager?

21. Which club have Rangers faced most often in European competition?

22. Between what years did Rangers have eight successive Scottish Cup final appearances?

23. Which two Rangers players share the record for most Scotland caps?

24. Celtic have won only one of the major domestic titles more often than Rangers. Which?

25. In what season did Rangers lose more games than they won – 1952–53, 1969–70, or 1985–86?

NINE IN A ROW

1. How many times did Rangers clinch the championship at Ibrox in the nine-in-a-row sequence?

2. Who scored a hat-trick in Rangers' victory over Aberdeen that clinched the club's eighth successive championship?

3. Who were Rangers' main title challengers in season 1994–95?

4. In what season did Tommy Burns' Celtic lose only one league game in their entire campaign, but still lose the title to Rangers?

5. Which three Rangers players played in every season of the nine in a row?

6. Gary McSwegan scored the goal that clinched the 1992–93 championship at which ground?

7. What was the points margin of Rangers' championship success against Aberdeen in the 1991 championship?

8. Who played just 13 games for Rangers, but helped the side to the first of their nine successive League Championships with two decisive goals in the league clincher?

9. Maurice Johnston was Rangers' top league goalscorer in which season?

10. Mark Walters was Rangers' top league goalscorer in which season?

11. During the League Championship of season 1993–94, Andy Goram had 17 shut-outs, but one other Rangers keeper had 11 shut-outs that year. Who?

12. Which side finished second to Rangers most often throughout the nine successive championships?

13. Which four sides finished second to Rangers through the nine-in-a-row period?

14. Which player was Rangers' biggest transfer acquisition in two different seasons?

15. Rangers' biggest league win through the nine-in-a-row was 7–0 against which side?

16. In how many of the nine successive championship seasons did Chris Woods tend the Rangers goal?

17. True or false – through the nine-in-a-row period, Ally McCoist was Rangers' top league goalscorer in only the two seasons in which he won the 'Golden Boot' as Europe's leading marksman?

18. Who was Rangers' most costly transfer acquisition through the nine-in-a-row championship seasons?

19. Over how many of the nine championships did Richard Gough skipper the side?

20. Rangers' biggest margin of victory in the championship through the nine successive seasons came in 1994–95. Which team finished in second place?

21. Which defender was signed from Vicenza in 1996 for £1.7 million?

22. In how many of the nine-in-a-row seasons did Jorg Albertz play for Rangers?

23. Who was the midfielder, signed from Morton, who played a vital role in the last of the nine championships?

24. Trevor Steven clinched one of the nine championship

victories with a well-placed headed goal at which ground?

25. What was Celtic's lowest finish in the league through Rangers' nine championships?

SKIPPERS

1. From which club was Lorenzo Amoruso signed?

2. Who became Rangers captain after John McClelland departed?

3. Which Rangers skipper's father played for Charlton Athletic?

4. When did Richard Gough win his first Scottish Premier Championship Winners' medal?

5. Which great Rangers skipper of the Struth era won 11 championship medals?

6. What decoration did John Greig receive from the Queen?

7. In what year did Terry Butcher play his last competitive game for Rangers?

8. How many championships did Richard Gough win?

9. How many Trebles did John Greig win as a player?

10. John Greig broke through to the Rangers first team on a tour to which country in 1962?

11. What was the last trophy John Greig won as a player and when did he win it?

12. How many domestic winners' medals did John Greig win – 14, 15 or 16?

13. Who relinquished the Rangers captaincy on the return of Richard Gough in 1997?

14. Who captained Scotland against England twice and won 15 caps between 1922 and 1933?

15. Which legendary captain went on to become a trainer and groundsman at Ibrox?

16. Who captained Scotland a record 48 times?

17. Which Rangers captain went on to become manager of Third Lanark?

18. Who was capped 40 times between 1952 and 1963?

19. Which full-back partner of Eric Caldow went on to captain Rangers and Scotland?

20. To which side was Richard Gough transferred when he left Rangers after securing the nine in a row?

21. Which former Rangers skipper went on to manage Sunderland?

22. Who did John Greig appoint as his first captain?

23. Which Rangers skipper was acquired from Hibernian?

24. Who was the Rangers captain in the 1984 League Cup win over Celtic?

25. Who stood in for John Greig as skipper when he was ruled out of the 1970 League Cup final?

MANAGERS

1. What was Jock Wallace's last game as manager of Rangers?

2. Up to and including Dick Advocaat, how many Rangers managers have there been?

3. From whom was Graeme Souness signed?

4. How many times did Souness win the Scottish Cup?

5. Which Rangers manager was a professional sprinter?

6. Which Rangers manager died in office?

7. Which trophy did Rangers boss Graeme Souness first win during his tenure?

8. Which Rangers manager went on to win a Scottish domestic trophy after leaving Ibrox?

9. Which American side did Dick Advocaat play for?

10. What was the significance of Rangers 3–1 defeat from Gornik Zabrze in 26 November 1969 that put them out of the European Cup Winners' Cup?

11. How did Rangers' first manager William Wilton's tenure as boss end?

12. For how long did Scot Symon hold the managerial reins at Ibrox?

13. For how long was Davie White manager of Rangers?

14. Who was the eighth man to manage Rangers?

15. What vital role did manager Willie Waddell have in the outcome of Rangers' away goals victory over Sporting Lisbon in November 1971?

16. What famous victory clinched Walter Smith's first championship as Rangers boss?

17. Who were the scorers when Rangers' win at Celtic Park all but clinched Dick Advocaat's first championship as Rangers boss?

18. Who took over as caretaker boss after the resignation of John Greig?

19. For how long did Bill Struth manage Rangers?

20. Who was the top goalscorer in John Greig's first season as manager?

21. Which side was the last to eliminate Walter Smith's Rangers from the European Cup?

22. Who won more Scottish Cups as Rangers boss – Walter Smith or Scot Symon?

23. What was Dick Advocaat's nickname, earned before he joined Rangers?

24. True or false – Scot Symon won more Scottish Cups than championships as Rangers boss?

25. Which two Rangers managers served part of their football career at Shawfield Stadium?

IBROX SUPREMOS

1. Who was Jock Wallace's assistant in his second stint at Ibrox?

2. Davie White won the League Cup with what side after leaving Ibrox?

3. Which Rangers boss was born in Milnathort, Fife?

4. Which Rangers boss had a spell as a sports journalist?

5. Who was John Greig's assistant, appointed in 1979?

6. Which side did Willie Waddell take to the Scottish First Division Championship?

7. Which two managers won the League Cup as bosses of sides other than Rangers?

8. Which Rangers boss was once a prospective Celtic signing as a youngster?

9. Who was the Rangers assistant boss who resigned after the dismissal of Scot Symon?

10. Which manager refused to sit behind the desk in the Manager's Room until he believed he had earned the right to?

11. What was Jock Wallace's last game as Rangers manager?

12. Which manager is credited with originating the *Rangers News*?

13. Jock Wallace left which side to take up a second stint as manager of Rangers?

14. How many domestic trophies did Willie Waddell win?

15. After Bill Struth, who was Rangers' longest-serving manager?

16. What was Dave White's last match as Rangers boss?

17. What was Jock Wallace's last match as manager of Rangers in 1978?

18. Who signed Alex Ferguson for Rangers?

19. Which former Rangers, Hearts and Falkirk player became a Scotland boss?

20. Who acted as caretaker manager when Davie White was sacked?

21. Who is the only caretaker manager of Rangers to have achieved a 100 per cent record in results?

22. Which Rangers boss had a home within sight of Ibrox?

23. Which Rangers boss played cricket for Scotland?

24. Who scored the first goal for Rangers under Walter Smith's leadership?

25. Which Rangers boss has won the Scottish Cup most often as manager?

THE BOSSES

1. When Rangers faced Sunderland in a testimonial match in 1993, who was the Roker Park boss?

2. Only two players have played under four managers at Ibrox. Name them.

3. Who won the championship in John Greig's last season as manager?

4. Who won the championship in Jock Wallace's last season as Rangers boss?

5. When did Souness take charge of the team at Ibrox – at the end of season 1985–86 or the beginning of the next?

6. Which of the legendary Ibrox bosses died in 1985?

7. Who was the first Rangers boss to use the manager's office in Ibrox?

8. Which club did Archie Knox leave to join Walter Smith at Ibrox?

9. Who scored Rangers' last goal under the management of Davie White?

10. Scot Symon took which side to the English FA Cup final?

11. How many Rangers bosses did not manage any other side in their careers?

12. Who was the Celtic boss who signed Alfie Conn?

13. Which team did Jim Forrest join when he left Ibrox, and what was the connection with Scot Symon?

14. Who was the Motherwell boss when they won the Scottish Cup in 1991?

15. Who was the former Rangers player who bossed Raith Rovers to their win over Celtic in the League Cup final of 1994?

16. Who was the first Rangers player to manage Scotland?

17. Who was the first former Rangers star to lead a team to the European Cup?

18. Who said 'Davie is a very fine man. He is with a wonderful club,' and what was the occasion?

19. Rangers legend Davie Meiklejohn went on to manage which club?

20. Which three managers won most League Cups for Rangers, with four each?

21. In what year did Willie Waddell take Kilmarnock to the Championships?

22. What interest did Rangers have in the managers in the 1960 Scottish Cup final?

23. Which Scottish side did Jock Wallace first appear for as a player?

24. Under which boss were the Rangers players first introduced to training at Gullane?

25. In what position did Willie Waddell serve Rangers as a player?

STRIKERS

1. Colin Stein was sent off at Ibrox following a clash with which Rangers player?

2. With which club did Mark Hateley win his first Championship medal?

3. What was the film that Ally McCoist made his acting debut in?

4. Which major star was left out of the 1981 Scottish Cup final with Davie Cooper, but returned for the replay?

5. How many goals did Andy Gray score for Rangers – three, four or five?

6. Former Rangers player Andy Gray won an English League Cup medal with which side?

7. How many Scottish Cup medals were won by Ally McCoist?

8. How many hat-tricks did Colin Stein score in his first three games?

9. Although Ally McCoist scored 49 goals in competition in 1992–93, two players scored more in Europe for Rangers that season. Who were they?

10. Who scored more goals in Europe during their time together at Ibrox, McCoist or Hateley?

11. Who scored more goals in Europe during their time together at Ibrox, McCoist or Johnston?

12. Alex Ferguson topped the Rangers scoring charts in what season?

13. Who scored the most goals for Rangers – Alex MacDonald, Colin Stein or Sandy Jardine?

14. Against which side did Sebastian Rozental score his first goal?

15. Who, in 1989, ended Ally McCoist's five-year run as top league goalscorer for Rangers?

16. Who scored two hat-tricks in four days against Clydebank, then Ilves Tampere, and went on to win four caps?

17. Who was the 'King of Ibrox Park' in the song the fans sang to the tune of 'Noel, Noel'?

18. Which striker of the Wallace Treble year in 1978 remained at Ibrox during Souness' first season?

19. True or false – Willie Thornton was the first post-war player to score 100 goals for the club?

20. Who was signed from a junior secondary school in Edinburgh for £20 and went on to become a prolific striker before leaving for Manchester City in 1965?

21. Which '60s strikers were related and often played together in the same Rangers side?

22. Who was signed from Aalborg in 1996 for £1.35 million?

23. Where did Gordon Durie begin his footballing career?

24. Ally McCoist beat which Dundee hit-man's record of post-war league goals?

25. Who was Rangers' top goalscorer for three successive seasons from 1956 to 1959?

TRANSFER MARKET

1. Who was Rangers first £100,000 signing?

2. Who was Rangers first £1 million signing?

3. Which two players were signed in a double swoop in 1985, with the fee decided by a tribunal?

4. Former Rangers captain John McClelland was signed from which English side?

5. A transfer deal involving Rangers stars Davie Wilson and Wilson Wood brought which player to Ibrox from Dundee United in the '60s?

6. Which player went to Dundee in the deal which took Andy Penman to Ibrox?

7. From which club was Stuart Munro signed?

8. From which side was Michael Mols signed?

9. Who was John Greig's last signing?

10. To which side was Graeme Roberts transferred when he left Ibrox?

11. Who did Souness sign from Bolton Wanderers and later transfer to Oxford United?

12. From which side was Trevor Francis signed?

13. Which winger was signed by Jock Wallace for £40,000 from St Mirren?

14. To which club was Derek Ferguson transferred when he departed Ibrox?

15. Who joined Rangers in 1987 from Maccabi for a fee of £100,000?

16. To which club was Maurice Johnston transferred when he departed Ibrox?

17. Who was signed to fill the midfield slot vacated by Trevor Steven's move to Marseilles?

18. Germany's transfer record was broken when Brian Laudrup moved from Bayer Uerdingen to what side?

19. Who was signed from Istanbulspor in 1996?

20. Which Ranger joined Durban City in South Africa when he left Ibrox in 1973?

21. Whose transfer from St Mirren at the age of 19 broke the Scottish record?

22. What was the transfer fee involved when Graeme Souness joined Rangers?

23. To which side was Mark Walters transferred when he left Rangers?

24. Who did Graeme Souness say that 'pound for pound' was his best signing at £250,000?

25. Who was John Greig's record signing from Hibernian?

SCOTTISH PREMIER LEAGUE

1. Rangers scored 17 goals in three concurrent matches in 1982 against which Premier League side?

2. Whose dismissal in an Old Firm match was followed by a late Celtic equaliser in 1997?

3. Which boss led Rangers to the first Premier League Championship?

4. Who sponsored the Scottish Premiership League immediately before the Bank of Scotland?

5. Who scored Rangers' first Premier League goal?

6. Apart from Celtic, which side has scored most Premier League goals against Rangers?

7. When Rangers won the title in 1975 it ended a barren spell of how long without the Championship?

8. Rangers won the first-ever Old Firm clash of the Premier League with Derek Johnstone scoring the opener in a 2–1 win. Which No 11 grabbed the winner?

9. Which midfielder was the first Rangers player to be ordered off in the Premier League?

10. How many Premier League Championships did Rangers compete in under Jock Wallace's managership?

11. In 1977, Rangers fought back at Ibrox from a 2–0 deficit to Celtic to win 3–2. Who scored the Rangers goals?

12. Rangers clinched their second Premier League title in 1978 with a win against which side at Ibrox?

13. Two players shared the penalty duties and scored two apiece in the 1978 season. Alex Miller was one, but who was the other?

14. Who scored the goal that secured Graeme Souness' first Premier Championship for Rangers?

15. Who suffered serious injury against Aberdeen at Ibrox which severely inhibited Rangers' title challenge in season 1987–88?

16. Which Rangers striker completed his single season at

Ibrox in 1989 with two goals in the penultimate match against Dundee?

17. Who captained Rangers to the championship in 1991 in the absence of the injured Richard Gough?

18. Who wore the Rangers No 9 jersey in the dramatic last-day decider against Aberdeen in 1991?

19. In what season did Rangers clinch the title with a 4–0 win against St Mirren at Ibrox?

20. Who scored a hat-trick to seal the championship for Rangers in 1996?

21. Who was Ranger's top league goalscorer in season 1995–96?

22. Which Rangers full-back opened the scoring in the Old Firm fixture at Celtic Park in season 1995–96?

23. Trevor Steven headed the decisive goal at Tannadice to give Rangers the title under which manager?

24. How many titles did Andy Goram win at Rangers?

25. Who were the first sponsors of the Premier League?

GOALKEEPERS

1. Which three goalkeepers shared the jersey in season 1997–98.

2. Which three goalkeepers played for Rangers in the Souness era?

3. Which four goalkeepers played under manager John Greig?

4. How many games did Chris Woods play without losing a goal, establishing a goalkeeping record?

5. How many goalkeepers did Walter Smith use in his first full season?

6. Who replaced Andy Goram as regular keep at Ibrox?

7. Who was understudy to Chris Woods at Ibrox?

8. Who was the Rangers keeper when Willie Waddell

took over?

9. Who was Rangers goalkeeper in the 1967 European Cup Winners' Cup final?

10. Name the four squad goalkeepers in the 1995–96 season.

11. How many times did Graeme Roberts play in goals for Rangers?

12. Who was the 'man in black'?

13. Which Rangers goalkeeper went on to manage Scotland?

14. Which keeper played cricket and football for Scotland?

15. Which keeper was at Ibrox for 12 years and never won a medal?

16. Who was in the Rangers goal for the 1961 European Cup Winners' Cup final?

17. Who was the reserve keeper on the bench in Barcelona for the 1972 European Cup Winners' Cup final?

18. Who was the goalkeeper in the defeat by Gornik

that ended Davie White's Rangers career?

19. In his first season as manager, how many keepers did John Greig use throughout the campaign?

20. Who was capped more for Scotland – Peter McCloy or Stewart Kennedy?

21. Which four goalkeepers played under Walter Smith in season 1994–95?

22. Who was the keeper when Rangers were ousted from the European Cup by AEK Athens in 1994?

23. Which Rangers goalkeeper made his Old Firm debut on the day that Celtic keeper John Thompson died?

24. Who was the famous Russian keeper who introduced a new style of goalkeeping to the crowds who followed the 1945 Dynamo Moscow tour?

25. In what year did Stefan Klos win a European Cup medal with Borussia Dortmund?

TROPHIES, DOUBLES and TREBLES

1. Which club put Rangers out of the Scottish Cup in Graeme Souness' first season at Ibrox?

2. Which two Rangers goalkeepers have won four Scottish Cup medals each?

3. Rangers' Championship win in 1999–2000 completed how many major trophies for the club throughout its history?

4. What was the last cup won by Greig as manager.

5. Which Rangers winger won seven League Cup medals?

6. Who was signed from Hibernian in a free transfer and went on to become a vital player in Jock Wallace's 1978 squad?

7. Who won a championship medal with Kilmarnock then went on to win two Trebles with Rangers?

8. Who scored the only goal of the Scottish Cup final to clinch a first Treble for Dick Advocaat?

9. In what year did Scot Symon lead Rangers to the Treble?

10. In what season did Walter Smith lead Rangers to the Treble?

11. Which prolific striker helped Rangers to their first Treble in 1949?

12. Who was the Rangers skipper who scored two penalties in the Scottish Cup final against Clyde in 1949 to complete the Treble?

13. Who did Rangers beat in the Scottish Cup to give Scot Symon the Treble?

14. In Symon's Treble year, Rangers clinched the League Cup with a four-goal display from which striker against which side?

15. Despite their domestic dominance, Rangers plunged out of the European Cup preliminary round at the hands of what great side in 1963?

16. Who was Rangers' goalkeeper throughout Symon's Treble season?

17. What double did John Greig secure in his first season as boss?

18. What double did Graeme Souness achieve in his first season and who were runners-up?

19. Souness narrowly missed out on a Treble in season 1988–89, when Rangers lost the Scottish Cup but victory over which side in the League Cup set up a Double?

20. In his last season at Ibrox, Souness left before he could see the Championship sealed, but he won the League Cup against which side?

21. In the 1992–93 Treble season, which side(s) provided the opposition in the cup finals?

22. Walter Smith completed a league and cup double in his first full season as boss. Which cup did he win and who were the opposition?

23. In 1993–94, Walter Smith missed out on back-to-back Trebles, but secured a double with victory in the League Cup over who?

24. Dick Advocaat missed out on his second Treble in 1999–2000, but victory over who secured the double?

25. How many Trebles have Rangers won?

MISCELLANEOUS

1. Which famous American Western hero once visited Ibrox?

2. Who won the Scottish Young Player of the Year award in season 1986–87?

3. Who won the Scottish Young Player of the Year award in season 1998–99?

4. Which Rangers player won a European Cup Winners' Cup medal with Aberdeen?

5. Which Rangers player won the Scottish First Division Player of the Year award in 1998–99?

6. How many Rangers players have won the Scottish Sportswriters Player of the Year award on two occasions?

7. Who is the only player to have won a Scottish Cup

Winners' medal under both Walter Smith and Dick Advocaat?

8. Who was the qualified chartered accountant who played in Walter Smith's side in the mid-'90s?

9. When did Chairman David Murray first take a major financial interest in Rangers?

10. What is the longest period the club went without a League Championship win?

11. Who scored two penalties in the final of the League Cup in 1984?

12. Who was the first non-Scottish Rangers player to win the Sportswriters Player of the Year award?

13. Who was the last German player to play for Rangers before Jorg Albertz?

14. What was the significance to Willie Waddell of the 1948 flight that Rangers took to Lisbon on their way to a friendly with Benfica?

15. Before he acquired an interest in Rangers, which Scottish club did David Murray attempt to buy?

16. Which boxer defended his World Lightweight title at Ibrox in 1980?

17. When was Rangers' stage play *Follow Follow* produced?

18. Who were the guest players who turned out for an Old Firm select in a Testimonial match against Scotland for the Ibrox disaster?

19. What was the colour of the Rangers away jersey in 1994–95?

20. Which Rangers player went on to be an administrator with the Scottish Professional Footballers Association?

21. Which former Rangers player went on to senior office in the Scottish Premier League?

22. Which English side did Rangers defeat in the Ibrox International Tournament in 1994?

23. Which great inside-forward, under Symon, won seven honours for Rangers and seven caps, but remained part-time throughout his career?

24. Who replaced Eric Caldow in the left-back slot?

25. Which former Rangers player went on to win the World Indoor Bowls Championship?

1. What did Jim Baxter and Allan Johnston have in common?

2. What do Dick Advocaat, Richard Gough and Willie Johnston have in common?

3. Which two goalkeepers faced Rangers in European competition then joined up at Ibrox?

4. Who scored twice for Rangers against Ajax in their Super Cup clash in the '70s?

5. Who was the last player to be signed from East Fife and break through to the Rangers first team?

6. Who was the first Rangers player to have competed in a European Cup final?

7. Who was voted the Young Player of the Tournament in the 1990 World Cup finals?

8. In what year did Ian Ferguson win a Scottish Cup medal for St Mirren?

9. Who is the last player to have scored a hat-trick against Rangers then join up at Ibrox?

10. Who was the Romanian defender who signed for Rangers but never made his first-class debut?

11. In which year did Rangers first tour North America?

12. Who is the only player to have represented Rangers and to have won the Player of the Year award in England?

13. Who was the first Dutch internationalist to play for Rangers?

14. What was unusual about the opposition in the Scott Nisbet Testimonial match?

15. Ruud Gullit was a star of the Feyenoord side that came to Ibrox in 1983. What other great Dutch star played that evening?

16. What do Real Sociedad and Porte Allegre have in common?

17. What do Iraq, Kuwait, Australia and New Zealand have in common?

18. When Rangers beat Everton in the Dubai Cup, the match was settled on penalties 8–7. How did the match finish after 90 minutes?

19. In their tour of Britain in 1945, Dynamo Moscow faced which other sides before meeting Rangers?

20. When did Rangers face Scotland in a challenge match?

21. Which foreign player scored his only Ibrox goal in a friendly against Rangers in the Souness era before he joined the club?

22. Who scored Rangers' first hat-trick in European competition?

23. What was the significance to Ally McCoist and Mark Falco of the 7–0 drubbing of Morton in 1987?

24. Who scored a hat-trick on his debut in a match against Eintracht Frankfurt in 1967?

25. In what year did the Premier League title race between Rangers and Celtic go down to the last game?

MULTIPLE CHOICE

1. Who scored more league goals – Greig, Parlane or Forrest?

2. The name of which famous club is not inscribed on the Scottish Cup – Rangers, Celtic or Queens Park?

3. Rangers travelled to which European country on a tour in 1912 – Denmark, Germany or France?

4. In which year was the first live transmission of the Scottish Cup final on television – 1973, 1977 or 1981?

5. For how long did Colin Stein's £100,000 signing remain a transfer record – 7, 11 or 14 years?

6. How many goals did Paul Gascoigne score in his first season at Ibrox – 19, 20 or 21?

7. How many Scottish Cup medals did Derek Johnstone win – three, four or five?

8. Which member of the Royal Family presented the Scottish Cup to John Greig after the 1973 final – Princess Anne, Princess Alexandra or Prince Philip?

9. How old was Paul Gascoigne when he joined Rangers – 26, 28 or 30?

10. How tall is Andy Goram – 5ft 10in, 5ft 11in or 6ft?

11. How many goals did Ally McCoist score in competition in 1992–93 – 45, 49 or 54?

12. How many domestic trophies did Davie Cooper win in his career – 12, 14 or 16?

13. What age was Alan McLaren when injury ended his career – 27,28 or 29?

14. How many former Rangers players were in the Hearts side that almost won the Title in 1986 – three, four or five?

15. Which full-back played most often on the same flank as Jim Baxter – Eric Caldow, Bobby Shearer or Harold Davis?

16. Who made his debut as a 15-year-old in the Tom Forsyth Testimonial – Billy Mackay, Bobby Russell, or Derek Ferguson?

17. Which pop-star icon took in an Old Firm match from the Govan Stand in 1994 – Robbie Williams, Cliff Richard or Bob Geldof?

18. When did the Rangers Social Club open – 1970, 1971 or 1972?

19. Which team stood between Rangers and back-to-back Trebles in 1994 – Celtic, Hibernian or Dundee United?

20. What was the format of the international tournament that Rangers participated in in Amsterdam in 1997 – five, six or seven-a-side?

21. George McLean, Willie Johnston and Jimmy Nicholl all played in which city for the local side – Vancouver, Toronto or Chicago?

22. Which former Rangers player played alongside Andy Goram at Oldham – Gordon Smith, Graeme Roberts or Mark Falco?

23. Apart from Celtic, which other club has the best league record against Rangers – Partick Thistle, Aberdeen or Morton?

24. Which of these never played at Ibrox – Gullit, Cruyff, Pele or Puskas?

25. Who is the odd one out – Nicklaus, Player or Palmer?

MIXED BAG

1. Who holds the Rangers record for goalkeeping appearances – Peter McCloy or Jerry Dawson?

2. From which club did Rangers sign Brian Laudrup?

3. Which Rangers player suffered a broken ankle in the 1–0 Scottish Cup defeat at Berwick in 1967?

4. From which club did Rangers receive the 'Loving Cup'?

5. In what year did Rangers receive the 'Loving Cup'?

6. What legendary English star represented Rangers for a short spell during the war years?

7. Who replaced Billy Ritchie in the Rangers goal in season 1966–67?

8. Who succeeded Kai Johansen in the Rangers No 2 jersey?

9. Which French side defeated Rangers home and away in season 1975–76?

10. Who wore the No 8 jersey through much of the Treble-winning 1977–78 season?

11. At which ground did Rangers seal the first Championship under Graeme Souness?

12. Who were the South African stars of the Rangers side in the '50s?

13. Which former Rangers player became a celebrated chef when he hung up his boots?

14. Which former Rangers player gained prominence worldwide as one of the 'Beirut hostages'?

15. Which defender wore a No 5 shirt and was ever-present through the 1995–96 campaign?

16. Which Morton star joined Rangers in 1973?

17. Rangers faced which side when they broke the attendance record for a Sunday domestic match in 1974 with a 65,000 crowd?

18. Who was signed by Bill Struth just before the Dynamo Moscow game in 1945, but was prevented from playing by the Russians?

19. Which team did Davy Wilson go on to manage when his playing career ended?

20. Which side did Ian McMillan go on to manage?

21. Who won the League and League Cup with Rangers and the Scottish Cup with Aberdeen?

22. From which side was Kai Johansen signed?

23. How old was Willie Johnston when he retired – 38, 39 or 40?

24. Who arrived at Ibrox as part of the deal that took George McLean to Dens Park?

25. Who provided the opposition in Rangers' last European tie under Graeme Souness?

1. Rangers paid Sampdoria £300,000 for whose transfer?

2. How many trophies did Willie Waddell win as manager of Rangers?

3. To which club did John McClelland move when he left Rangers?

4. Which Celtic player was sent off in the first League Cup final of 1986, that Graeme Souness contested as manager?

5. In what year did Rangers sign Mo Johnstone?

6. Rangers' victory in the 1990 Ne'erday fixture at Celtic Park was the first at Parkhead in 16, 18 or 20 years?

7. Where did Oleg Kuznetsov incur the serious injury that eventually limited his Ibrox career?

8. Which three Rangers players were ordered off in the 1991 Scottish Cup defeat by Celtic at Parkhead?

9. Which Rangers boss sold Trevor Steven to Marseilles?

10. What precipitated the transfer of Chris Woods from Rangers and the acquisition of Andy Goram?

11. Who was ordered off after only a few minutes of the 1992 Scottish Cup semi-final tie with Celtic?

12. A mix-up between what two players opened the way for Craig Brewster to give Dundee United the solitary goal and Scottish Cup in 1993–94?

13. When did Rangers inflict a 2–0 defeat on Celtic for their only loss of the season?

14. When Mark Hateley left Rangers in 1995, he joined up with what Rangers star and where?

15. Which Cypriot team did Rangers defeat to qualify for the 1995–96 Champions League group phase?

16. Which lowly Scottish First Division side took Rangers to a replay in the 1982 semi-final of the Scottish Cup?

17. Which Spanish side eliminated Rangers from the European Cup Winners' Cup in 1979?

18. Which side took Rangers to two replays in the 1976 League Cup quarter-final and led to the transfer of one of the opposition to the Ibrox side?

19. With how many senior clubs has Ronald de Boer played with his brother Frank?

20. Who was the regular Rangers striker before Jimmy Miller?

21. Two of Rangers' Barcelona heroes had golf handicaps of five and under at the time of the match. Who were they?

22. Which Yugoslav club did Gordon Petric first play for?

23. With which English team did Trevor Steven begin his senior career?

24. With which Scottish club did John Brown begin his senior career?

25. What is the origin of the bicycle in the Ibrox Trophy Room?

ANSWERS

2001–2002 SQUAD

1. Borussia Dortmund.
2. Peter van Vossen.
3. Christian Nerlinger.
4. Arthur Numan.
5. Both played for Dundee.
6. Newcastle United.
7. Dave Mitchell.
8. Tommy McLean.
9. Murray Park.
10. Wouters signed Arveladze for Ajax.
11. Neil McCann.
12. Trinidad and Tobago.
13. Arthur Numan.
14. Manchester City.
15. Kenny Miller.
16. Aberdeen.
17. Arveladze and de Boer.
18. Ronald de Boer.
19. M. K. Maribor.

20. Alex Scott.
21. Shota Arveladze.
22. Ten.
23. Three – Arveladze, Vidmar, Lovenkrands.
24. Both played for Chelsea.
25. Tony Vidmar.

HISTORY

1. On 17 February 1894 Rangers won the Scottish Cup for the first time in their history, beating their Old Firm rivals in the process.
   Rangers 3 (McCreadie, Barker, McPherson) v Celtic 1 – Scottish Cup final.
2. Dynamo Moscow, the pride of Russia, met the Scottish Champions Rangers on 28 November 1945.
   Rangers 2 (Smith, Young) v Dynamo Moscow 2.
3. Victory ended Rangers' 25-year 'hoodoo' with the return of the Scottish Cup to Ibrox after a prolonged absence.
   Rangers 4 (Archibald (2), Meiklejohn, McPhail) v Celtic 0 – Scottish Cup final.
4. The great structure which provides the famous red

brick façade to the stadium was opened on 1 January 1929 with a fixture against Celtic, which the Light Blues won 3–0.

5. Celtic goalkeeper John Thomson tragically lost his life after his head collided with Rangers striker Sam English's knee in a 50–50 challenge. He died later in hospital of a depressed fracture of the skull. English, while unhurt, never recovered from the tragic event.
6. Rangers recorded nine successive championships through the war years. Rangers' sequence began in 1938–39 and continued through the war years until 1946–47. Although the wartime records are often deemed unofficial, the achievement was remarkable nevertheless.
7. Rangers were awarded the trophy after Celtic refused to abide by the rules and play the Cup final replay at Ibrox, stating that it should be held at Celtic Park after the first game was drawn at Rangers' home ground. They withdrew from the competition and Rangers were awarded the trophy.
8. The final ended in a riot when the fans of both sides demanded that the two teams play out extra-time after their second game had been drawn. The fans went on the rampage, burning turnstiles and battling with the police. The two teams agreed that the trophy should be withheld for that season, the only time it was never awarded to a side.
9. It was the date of the 'Ibrox Disaster', when 66 fans

lost their lives on the infamous 'Stairway 13'.

10. Rangers voted to incorporate the club in May 1899, releasing the finance that would fund the construction of Ibrox Stadium.
11. One of the founders, Moses McNeil, liked the name 'Rangers', having heard of an English rugby club with the same name.
12. Vale of Leven.
13. Dunfermline Athletic.
14. Double-glazing firm CR Smith.
15. Dumbarton in 1890.
16. Rangers completed their 18-game programme by winning every match.
17. 1968–69.
18. Tom Forsyth and Sandy Jardine.
19. Davie Cooper.
20. Max Murray.
21. The club's biggest victory (14–2) came against the Perthshire side in 1934.
22. Norrie Martin.
23. Preston North End.
24. 1966–67.
25. Jim Forrest, who was replaced by Jimmy Millar.

IN THE PAST

1. 1891.
2. Bob Wilson.
3. 1893.
4. Kinning Park.
5. Twenty-five years.
6. Winston Churchill.
7. On the occasion of the first match at Ibrox after the New Year.
8. Willie Waddell.
9. Hearts.
10. Five (Struth, White, Wallace, Smith, Advocaat).
11. Pony-driven mower.
12. Blue and white hoops.
13. Fifth, most recently in 1985–86.
14. South African Johnny Hubbard.
15. It was to be his last.
16. They served at Bellahouston Hospital tending the casualties, Struth as a physio and Wilton as an administrator.
17. Willie Waddell.
18. Sammy Cox.
19. Harold Davis.
20. Sammy Baird.
21. Orjan Persson.

22. Top.
23. Sunderland.
24. Austria Vienna, in 1933.
25. Burnbank.

CUP FINALS

1. Willie Johnston.
2. Alfie Conn and Derek Parlane.
3. Danish full-back Kai Johansen in the replayed final of 1966.
4. Aberdeen.
5. Ronnie McKinnon.
6. Nigel Spackman.
7. Rangers 1, Fiorentina 4.
8. Jim Stewart.
9. Gordan Petric and Alex Cleland.
10. Celtic.
11. 7–1 in the 1957 final against Celtic.
12. Morton (5–0).
13. 4–0, in 1928.
14. Davie Cooper.
15. Tory Gillick.

16. Maurice Johnston.
17. Four.
18. Eric Caldow.
19. Victory Cup.
20. Jardine, Grieg.
21. Jimmy Miller.
22. Willie Henderson.
23. Johnstone, Jardine and Jackson.
24. 1976.
25. Gordon Durie.

EUROPE

1. Fiorentina.
2. OG Nice in 1956.
3. Newcastle United.
4. They went out of the tournament despite being unbeaten.
5. Mario Kempes.
6. Alania Vladikavka.
7. Sparta Prague.
8. Rangers first, it was 1–0, 2–0, 3–0, 3–1, 3–2.
9. Colin Jackson.

10. Ajax and Borussia Dortmund.
12. European Super Cup.
13. They had to change the sponsor's name because of a prohibition on drinks advertising.
14. AEK Athens.
15. Finnish side, Ilves Tampere.
16. Alex MacDonald and Derek Johnstone.
    PSV Eindhoven 2 v Rangers 3 (MacDonald, Johnstone, Russell) – European Cup, Second Round, 1 November 1978.
17. AC Milan.
18. Borussia Munchengladbach.
19. Dave McPherson.
20. Wolverhampton Wanderers.
21. Sepp Maier.
22. 7–2.
23. Mark Hateley.
24. Borussia Dortmund.
25. Athletico Osasuna

CONTINENTAL EUROPE

1. AC Milan.

2. Graeme Souness.
3. Lubanski.
4. Manchester City.
5. Seville.
6. Willie Henderson.
7. Brian Heron.
8. UEFA Cup (1980–81).
9. All played for AC Milan.
10. Twelve games.
11. Juventus.
12. Glentoran.
13. Torino.
14. Wolverhampton Wanderers.
15. Real Saragossa.
16. Stuart McCall.
17. Atletico Osasuna.
18. Bayern Munich.
19. John Greig.
20. Graeme Souness reduced the width of the pitch.
21. Eintracht Frankfurt.
22. Sporting Lisbon.
23. Sparta Rotterdam.
24. Red Star Belgrade (1964–65).
25. Rangers won 3–1, but lost out 3–4 on aggregate.

OLD FIRM

1. Rangers recorded their biggest victory over Celtic in a league tie on 1 January 1943. The Light Blues won 8–1! It is the biggest margin of victory between the sides.
2. Alfie Conn.
3. Three.
4. Liam Brady (Inter Milan).
5. Scotland and an Old Firm Select.
6. Alfie Conn.
7. Davie Cooper.
8. Twice.
9. Jimmy and Derek Parlane.
10. Derek Johnstone.
11. 1979.
12. Jimmy Duncanson.
13. Ally McCoist.
14. Craig Moore.
15. Mark Walters.
16. Cammy Fraser.
17. 1–1.
18. Kenny Dalglish.
19. Pierre van Hooijdonk.
20. Alan McLaren.
21. They both scored at Celtic Park on their debut.

22. 1984 League Cup and 1986 Glasgow Cup.
23. George Niven.
24. 1888, the year of the Celts' formation.
25. Three.

NICKNAMES

1. Jimmy Millar and Ralph Brand, '50s and '60s strike partnership.
2. Sandy Jardine.
3. Alex Miller.
4. Willie Johnston.
5. Giovanni van Bronckhurst.
6. Initially George Young and latterly Eric Caldow.
7. John Greig.
8. Davie Cooper.
9. John Brown and Colin Jackson.
10. William Struth.
11. Ted McMinn.
12. Willie Waddell.
13. Ian McMillan.
14. Bud Flanagan – Willie Johnston (see 4 above).
15. Captain Cutlass.

16. George McLean.
17. Willie Mathieson.
18. Billy Ritchie.
19. Jazzer.
20. Ian Durrant.
21. Dave McPherson.
22. Robert Russell.
23. Tom Forsyth.
24. 'Coop' or 'Super'.
25. Alex Macdonald.

LEGENDS

1. Alan Morton.
2. Willie Telfer.
3. Sixteen.
4. Sunderland and Nottingham Forrest.
5. Fiorentina.
6. Kansas City Wiz.
7. Terry Butcher. After the loss of their influential skipper, Rangers lost impetus in the League, finishing behind Celtic.
8. 'Mo' joined Rangers on 10 July 1989 from Nantes.

9. Ally McCoist in 1983.
10. The late great Davie Cooper scored what has been called Rangers' greatest goal in the Dryborough Cup final in August 1979. Copper juggled the ball inside the penalty area, brushing defenders aside before sliding the ball into the net.
11. John Greig.
12. Chelsea, for £20,000.
13. Davie White.
14. Rapid Vienna.
15. Alex Scott.
16. Ian McCall.
17. Three.
18. Eric Caldow.
19. Italy.
20. Scotland.
21. His uncle, Ebbe Skovdahl, who became Aberdeen Manager.
22. Sheffield Wednesday.
23. They have both played for SV Hamburg.
24. John Greig, Sandy Jardine and Brian Laudrup.
25. John Brown.

IBROX GREATS

1. John Brown.
2. Davie Cooper.
3. John Greig.
4. Sandy Jardine.
5. Three.
6. Neil McCann and Gordon Petric.
7. Derek Johnstone.
8. Ian McColl.
9. Ralph Brand.
10. Scot Symon.
11. Jock Wallace.
12. John Greig.
13. Willie Thornton.
14. Alex Scott.
15. Arsenal.
16. Everton.
17. 1995.
18. 1992.
19. Jerry Dawson.
20. Andy Goram.
21. Bob McPhail.
22. Jerry Dawson.
23. Derek Johnstone.
24. Mark Hateley.

25. Willie Thornton.

ICONS

1. Falkirk.
2. Willie Woodburn.
3. Sandy Jardine.
4. £17,500.
5. Alex Scott.
6. Johnny Hubbard.
7. Ralph Brand.
8. Coventry City.
9. Richard Gough.
10. Yes.
11. Willie Henderson.
12. Colin Stein.
13. John Greig.
14. John Brown.
15. Swansea City.
16. Terry Butcher.
17. Arbroath.
18. Alex MacDonald.
19. Bobby Shearer.

20. Paul Gascoigne.
21. Alan Morton won ten to Bob McPhail's nine.
22. Queens Park.
23. Twenty-four.
24. John Greig (11).
25. All originated from Airdrie and played for the local side.

STADIUM

1. Five – Fleshers Haugh, Burnbank, Kinning Park, Old Ibrox, New Ibrox.
2. 1902.
3. 118,000.
4. Edmiston Drive.
5. No.
6. Copland, Broomloan, Govan and Main Stand.
7. Argentina.
8. 'Ready'.
9. The Queen Mary.
10. Half-mile race.
11. Rangers FC.
12. They were temporary cabins adjacent to the tunnel

as construction work continued on the stand.

13. In a greenhouse located between the stand and the east terracing.
14. Ibrox Stadium.
15. It was the billiard room.
16. Poland. It was received from Katowice.
17. 1988.
18. The end of timber terracings and a move towards earthbanks.
19. Boris.
20. White with some dark flecks.
21. 1998.
22. Copland Stand.
23. 1995–96.
24. Liverpool.
25. 1991.

HITMEN

1. Jim Forrest.
2. 1995.
3. Oleg Salenko.
4. Stein.

5. Gordon Smith.
6. Maurice Johnston.
7 Jim Forrest.
8. John Greig.
9. Jimmy Miller (4).
10. Jim Forrest (83) against Stein's 64.
11. In Scotland's 5–0 defeat by Portugal.
12. John Robertson. His brother was Chris Robertson who had a spell with the Ibrox side in the early '80s.
13. 1983.
14. Peter McCloy.
15. Oleg Salenko.
16. Bobby Williamson.
17. Chelsea and Spurs.
18. Derek Johnstone.
19. Jimmy Millar.
20. Stephane Gui'varch.
21. Gordon Dalziel.
22. Martin Henderson.
23. Willie Thornton.
24. Coventry City.
25. Alex Ferguson.

THE '70s

1. Colin Stein and Gordon Smith.
2. Four years.
3. John Greig.
4. One (Dundee).
5. Hibs.
6. Iain Munro.
7. The League Cup with a 2–1 win over Aberdeen.
8. Jim Denny.
9. Gordon Smith.
10. Tennent Caledonian Cup.
11. None. They won the Scottish Cup a year later, but the European Cup Winners' Cup had been returned by then.
12. Sandy Jardine.
13. Robert Russell.
14. St Etienne.
15. Aberdeen and Celtic.
16. Cologne.
17. Colin Stein.
18. Willie Henderson.
19. Rennes.
20. Stewart Kennedy.
21. Gordon Smith.
22. Valencia.

23. Alex Forsyth.
24. Texaco Cup.
25. Young Boys of Berne.

THE '80s

1. Graeme Souness.
2. Iain Ferguson.
3. John Greig.
4. Jock Wallace.
5. Motherwell.
6. Gordon Smith.
7. 0–0.
8. Season 1981–82, in the Scottish League Cup win over Dundee United.
9. John McClelland.
10. Derek Ferguson.
11. Sandy Clark.
12. Forfar Athletic.
13. Ally Dawson.
14. Ally McCoist.
15. Gough, Kirkwood and Dodds.
16. Dougie Bell.

17. Mansfield Town.
18. John Greig.
19. Malmo.
20. Gregor Stevens.
21. Craig Paterson.
22. Tommy McLean.
23. Lokeren (Belgium).
24. Bobby Williamson.
25. Queen of the South.

THE '90s

1. Ian McCall.
2. True.
3. Maurice Johnston and Stuart McCall (then with Everton).
4. Gordon Durie.
5. Goram, Stevens, Robertson, Gough, Spackman and Brown.
6. Neil Murray.
7. Celtic Park.
8. Alex Cleland and Gary Bollan.
9 Dave MacPherson.

10. Mark Hateley.
11. Tottenham Hotspur.
12. Davie Cooper.
13. Davie Cooper.
14. Davie Robertson and Steven Wright.
15. Staale Stensaas.
16. Tannadice Park.
17. Duncan Ferguson.
18. Erik Bo Andersen.
19. Sebastian Rozental.
20. Andy Goram.
21. Andy Dibble.
22. Marco Negri.
23. Antti Niemi.
24. Alexei Mikhailitcenko.
25. Highland League side, Keith.

CHAMPIONS LEAGUE

1. Ian Durrant.
2. Fraser Wishart.
3. Dale Gordon.
4. One. (Rod Wallace.)

5. Fabien Barthez.
6. 3 – Lyngby, Leeds United, Club Brugge.
7. Moscow was snowbound.
8. Anorthosis.
9. True.
10. Borussia Dortmund.
11. Rudi Voller.
12. Levski Sofia.
13. Jonatan Johansen.
14. Michael Mols and Jorg Albertz.
15. Parma.
16. Joachim Bjorklund.
17. Derek McInnes.
18. True – he scored a penalty to give PSV their only goal in a 4–1 defeat.
19. He scored in the final minute to give Bayern Munich a point and deny Rangers a vital home win in the Champions League competition.
20. Ronald de Boer.
21. Borussia Dortmund.
22. AEK Athens.
23. Steau Bucharest.
24. Sturm Graz.
25. Monaco.

INTERNATIONAL CAPS

1. Alex Miller.
2. John Greig, Ron McKinnon and Jim Baxter.
3. Thor Beck.
4. Cyprus.
5. Dave Mitchell.
6. Davy Wilson.
7. Colin Jackson.
8. Davie Cooper.
9. John Brown.
10. Peter McCloy.
11. Tom Forsyth.
12. Sammy Baird.
13. Davie Cooper.
14. John McClelland.
15. Ally McCoist. Gough has the same number, but some of his caps were earned at Dundee United.
16. Alan Morton.
17. Ritchie received one cap.
18. Sweden's Orjan Persson.
19. Provan with five caps.
20. Ralph Brand.
21. Gary Stevens.
22. Richard Gough.
23. Ray Wilkins.

24. Colin Stein, in 1969.
25. Tom Forsyth, Sandy Jardine and Derek Johnstone.

BARCELONA

1. Dave Smith.
2. Alfie Conn.
3. Colin Stein.
4. One, Alex MacDonald.
5. Four (Alfie Conn, Willie Johnston, Colin Stein, Derek Johnstone).
6. Two years, later commuted to one year after appeal.
7. Ronnie McKinnon.
8. Dave Smith.
9. Yes, they returned there for a friendly.
10. 35,000.
11. Johnston scored in 49 minutes.
12. Alfie Conn.
13. John Greig and Alfie Conn.
14. Sporting Lisbon.
15. Alfie Conn.
16. True.
17. Willie Henderson.

18. Tom Forsyth.
19. Paul Breitner.
20. Yes. Despite being banned for a year, they played Ajax in the Super Cup.
21. Fiorentina and Bayern Munich.
22. 1945.
23. Derek Johnstone.
24. Willie Johnston.
25. Muller, Beckenbauer and Maier.

CLASSIC MATCHES

1. Tom Forsyth scored the winner to give Rangers a 3–2 win over Celtic in the centenary Scottish Cup final in 1973.
2. John Greig.
3. He scored the equaliser in the final minute of the Old Firm clash of 17 October 1987 after the early dismissal of goalkeeper Chris Woods left Rangers with a rearguard battle, with central defender Graham Roberts in goal.
4. Terry Butcher, Chris Woods, Graeme Roberts and Celtic's Frank MacAvennie.

5. Rangers 3 (Johnston (2), Stein) v Dynamo Moscow 2. Rangers won the European Cup Winners' Cup at the Nou Camp Stadium in Barcelona.
6. Celtic 0 v Rangers 1 (Laudrup).
   Victory virtually sealed Rangers ninth successive championship, leaving the champions eight points clear of their rivals with few matches remaining.
7. Ally McCoist and Mark Hateley.
8. Ian Redford.
9. Graeme Souness.
10. Everton.
11. 1963.
12. He noticed that the Russians had twelve men on the field.
13. Aberdeen in the Scottish Cup final, at Celtic Park.
14. Robert Fleck.
15. Colin Stein at Easter Road.
16. Davie Meiklejohn.
17. George Young.
18. Kilmarnock.
19. Morton.
20. Bert Slater.
21. George McLean.
22. At right-midfield (right-half), wearing a No 4 jersey.
23. John Greig.
24. Neil McCann (2) and Jorg Albertz.
25. League Cup final.

ODD ONE OUT

1. Trevor Steven – the others played with Tottenham Hotspur.
2. Konterman – the others have played in Germany.
3. Russell.
4. Harold Davis.
5. Ronnie McKinnon.
6. John McClelland.
7. Sandy Clark.
8. Stewart Kennedy.
9. Colin Stein.
10. Jim Stewart.
11. Willie Johnston.
12. Beck. He was an Icelander, the others were Swedish.
13. Juventus is the only side which Rangers have ousted from European competition.
14. Struth.
15. 1997, the rest were Treble-winning years.
16. Wilton, Waddell and Souness.
17. Numan, who never played with Bayern Munich.
18. Jardine. All of the rest left Ibrox then returned to play again at Rangers.
19. Arthur Numan.
20. Dynamo Tbilisi.
21. Rapid Vienna.

22. Airdrie.
23. Aberdeen finished runners-up more often.
24. Jonas Thern.
25. Man of many clubs, Johnston did not play for Notts County.

GRAEME SOUNESS

1. Tottenham Hotspur.
2. Celtic.
3. Galatasaray.
4. Ally McCoist.
5. Two.
6. Jan Bartram.
7. League Cup.
8. George McCluskey.
9. League match against St Johnstone.
10. Avi Cohen.
11. Aston Villa.
12. Three.
13. Colin West.
14. Uruguay.
15. Dunfermline Athletic.

16. Julian Sprott.
17. Terry Butcher.
18. Ian Andrews.
19. 1988.
20. Stuart Munro.
21. The League opener against Hibs in 1986 when he was sent off.
22. Trevor Steven.
23. Phil Boersma.
24. Aberdeen.
25. True.

WALTER SMITH

1. AC Milan.
2. Scott Wilson was born in March 1977, with Ferguson in February 1978.
3. Staale Stensaas.
4. Zero.
5. Seb Rozental.
6. Sparta Prague.
7. Ashfield.
8. Dumbarton.

9. Andy Goram.
10. Alex Ferguson, during the 1986 World Cup finals in Mexico.
11. Scottish Cup – Airdrie.
12. Twelve.
13. Paul Gascoigne – £4.3 million.
14. The championship that provided the completion of Rangers' 'nine in a row'.
15. Three.
16. Airdrie, Hearts and Aberdeen.
17. 1995–96.
18. Rino Gattuso.
19. Fourteen.
20. Three.
21. Scottish Cup final against Hearts at Celtic Park.
22. OBE.
23. Jimmy Millar.
24. 1997.
25. Strasbourg.

DICK ADVOCAAT

1. Michael Mols, from FC Utrecht.

2. 1949.
3. Four years.
4. Once.
5. World Cup finals in USA.
6. League Cup, against St Johnstone.
7. Shelbourne Rovers.
8. Ruud Gullit.
9. Bobby Robson.
10. Borussia Munchengladbach.
11. FC Twente.
12. Chelsea.
13. As Dutch national coach, he came to watch Rangers star Peter Huistra in action.
14. Chicago Sting.
15. Sparta Rotterdam.
16. Klos.
17. Edinburgh.
18. Numan was born in December 1969. Mols was born a year later.
19. Many wore orange to salute Advocaat and his Dutch contingent.
20. Parma.
21. Bayer Leverkeusen.
22. Wolfsburg (Germany).
23. Aberdeen.
24. Seven.
25. Valencia.

RECORD BREAKERS

1. Jimmy Smith (300 goals between 1928 and 1946).
2. Dougie Gray.
3. Twenty-one points.
4. Aberdeen, Hibernian, Dundee United.
5. John Greig.
6. Peter McCloy.
7. Once (1991–92).
8. Eighteen.
9. Twenty-seven.
10. Gordon Durie.
11. John Greig (6).
12. Sandy Jardine.
13. Eintracht Frankfurt.
14. 10–0 against Valletta, in 1983.
15. True.
16. Eric Caldow.
17. Davie White.
18. Fifth, most recently in 1986.
19. John Greig.
20. William Struth (34 years).
21. Bayern Munich.
22. 1975 and 1983.
23. Richard Gough and Ally McCoist.
24. Scottish Cup.

25. 1985–86.

NINE IN A ROW

1. Three.
2. Paul Gascoigne in the 3–1 victory over Aberdeen on 28 April 1996.
3. Motherwell.
4. 1995–96.
5. Gough, Ferguson, McCoist.
6. Airdrie's Broomfield Stadium.
7. Two points.
8. Mel Sterland.
9. 1989–90 (15 goals).
10. 1990–91 (12 goals).
11. Ally Maxwell.
12. Aberdeen.
13. Celtic, Hearts, Motherwell and Aberdeen.
14. Trevor Steven.
15. Hibernian
16. Three.
17. True.
18. Paul Gascoigne – £4.3 million.

19. Seven.
20. Motherwell.
21. Joachim Bjorkland.
22. One.
23. Derek McInnes.
24. Tannadice Park.
25. Fifth, in season 1989–90.

SKIPPERS

1. Fiorentina.
2. Craig Paterson.
3. Richard Gough.
4. 1983, with Dundee United.
5. Davie Meiklejohn.
6. MBE.
7. 1990.
8. Ten.
9. Three.
10. Russia.
11. Scottish Cup in 1978.
12. Fifteen.
13. Brian Laudrup.

14. Davie Meiklejohn.
15. Jock Shaw.
16. George Young.
17. George Young.
18. Eric Caldow.
19. Bobby Shearer.
20. Kansas City Wiz.
21. Terry Butcher.
22. Derek Johnstone.
23. Craig Paterson.
24. John McClelland.
25. Ronnie McKinnon.

MANAGERS

1. A friendly encounter with Tottenham Hotspur in April 1986.
2. Ten.
3. Sampdoria.
4. None.
5. William Struth.
6. William Wilton was drowned in 1920 while manager of Rangers.

7. Glasgow Cup with a 3–2 win over Celtic.
8. Davie White won the League Cup with Dundee in 1973.
9. Chicago Sting.
10. It signalled the end of Davie White's tenure as manager.
11. He was lost at sea in a boating accident in May 1920.
12. Thirteen years (1954–67).
13. Two years (1967–69).
14. Graeme Souness.
15. He brandished the rule book at match officials as his side were led into a penalty shoot-out in Lisbon after Rangers had lost 4–3 after extra-time in the return leg of the second-round tie to go level in aggregate against Sporting Lisbon. Waddell pointed out that away goals count double in extra-time, which gave the tie to Rangers.
16. A depleted Rangers side showed immense courage to record a last-day win against title rivals Aberdeen. Rangers 2 (Hateley (2)) v Aberdeen 0 – Premier League Championship.
17. Neil McCann (2) and Jorg Albertz.
    Celtic 0 v Rangers 3 (McCann (2), Albertz) – 2 May 1999.
18. Tommy McLean.
19. Thirty-four years.
20. Gordon Smith.
21. Gothenburg.

22. Symon won five, while Smith won three.
23. The Little General.
24. True.
25. William Struth and Davie White.

IBROX SUPREMOS

1. Alex Totten.
2. Dundee.
3. William Struth.
4. Willie Waddell.
5. Joe Mason.
6. Kilmarnock.
7. Scot Symon (East Fife) and Davie White (Dundee).
8. Graeme Souness.
9. Bobby Seith.
10. Davie White.
11. Tottenham Hotspur (2–0 defeat).
12. Willie Waddell.
13. Motherwell.
14. Two (one at Kilmarnock).
15. William Wilton.
16. European Cup Winners' Cup tie against Gornik at

Ibrox.

17. Scottish Cup final v Aberdeen.
18. Scot Symon.
19. John Prentice.
20. Willie Thornton.
21. Willie Thornton.
22. William Struth.
23. Scot Symon.
24. Sandy Robertson.
25. William Struth.

THE BOSSES

1. Terry Butcher.
2. Peter McCloy and Derek Johnstone – played under Waddell, Wallace, Greig and Souness.
3. Aberdeen.
4. Celtic.
5. He took official charge of the side for the last Premier League match of 1985–86 season.
6. Scot Symon, aged 74.
7. William Struth.
8. Manchester United.

9. Jim Baxter.
10. Preston North End.
11. Three (Wilton, Struth, Greig).
12. Jock Stein.
13. Forrest went to Preston North End, formerly bossed by Symon.
14. Tommy McLean.
15. Jimmy Nicholl.
16. Ian McColl.
17. Alex Ferguson as manager, Graeme Souness as a player.
18. Scot Symon speaking of Davie White after his appointment as manager.
19. Partick Thistle.
20. Souness, Symon and Wallace.
21. 1965.
22. Rangers boss was Scot Symon and opponents Kilmarnock were managed by former Ranger Willie Waddell who later became Rangers manager.
23. Airdrie.
24. Willie Waddell.
25. Outside-right.

STRIKERS

1. Alex Ferguson.
2. Monaco.
3. *A Shot at Glory*.
4. Derek Johnstone.
5. Five.
6. Wolves.
7. One.
8. Two.
9. Durrant and Hateley.
10. Hateley (8) McCoist (7).
11. Johnston (5) McCoist (3).
12. 1967–68 (twenty-seven goals).
13. Alex MacDonald.
14. St Johnstone.
15. Kevin Drinkell.
16. Robert Fleck.
17. Derek Parlane.
18. Derek Johnstone.
19. True.
20. Ralph Brand.
21. Alex Willoughby and Jim Forrest, who were cousins.
22. Erik Bo Anderson.
23. East Fife.
24. Gordon Wallace.

25. Max Murray.

TRANSFER MARKET

1. Colin Stein.
2. Richard Gough.
3. Iain Ferguson and Cammy Fraser, from Dundee.
4. Mansfield Town, for £90,000.
5. Orjan Persson.
6. George McLean.
7. Alloa Athletic, for £15,000 in 1984.
8. FC Utrecht.
9. Jimmy Nicholl.
10. Chelsea.
11. Jimmy Philips.
12. Atalanta.
13. Bobby McKean.
14. Hearts.
15. Avi Cohen.
16. Everton.
17. Stuart McCall.
18. Bayern Munich, in 1992 for £2.2 million.
19. Peter van Vossen.

20. Ronnie McKinnon.
21. George McLean.
22. £300,000.
23. Liverpool.
24. Ray Wilkins.
25. £225,000 acquisition Craig Paterson.

SCOTTISH PREMIER LEAGUE

1. Kilmarnock.
2. Paul Gascoigne.
3. Jock Wallace.
4. Bells Whisky.
5. Derek Johnstone.
6. Aberdeen.
7. Eleven years.
8. Quinton Young.
9. Alex MacDonald.
10. Three.
11. Gordon Smith (2) and Derek Johnstone.
12. Motherwell.
13. Sandy Jardine.
14. Terry Butcher.

15. Terry Butcher.
16. Andy Gray.
17. Nigel Spackman.
18. Mark Hateley.
19. 1991–92.
20. Paul Gascoigne.
21. Gordon Durie.
22. Alex Cleland.
23. Graeme Souness.
24. Six.
25. DIY merchants, B&Q.

GOALKEEPERS

1. Snelders, Goram and Niemi.
2. Woods, Walker and Ginzberg.
3. McCloy, Young, Stuart, Bruce.
4. Eleven.
5. One.
6. Stefan Klos.
7. Nicky Walker.
8. Gerry Neef.
9. Norrie Martin.

10. Goram, Scott, Snelders, Thomson.
11. Twice.
12. Sorensen.
13. Bobby Brown.
14. Andy Goram.
15. Norrie Martin.
16. Billy Ritchie.
17. Gerry Neef.
18. Gerry Neef.
19. Just one – Peter McCloy played in every game.
20. Stewart Kennedy.
21. Goram, Maxwell, Scott and Thomson.
22. Andy Goram.
23. Jerry Dawson.
24. 'Tiger' Khomich.
25. 1997.

TROPHIES, DOUBLES and TREBLES

1. Hamilton Accies.
2. Peter McCloy and Billy Ritchie.
3. One hundred.
4. League Cup.

5. Davie Cooper.
6. Johnny Hamilton.
7. Tommy McLean.
8. Rod Wallace.
9. 1964.
10. 1992–93.
11. Willie Thornton.
12. George Young.
13. Dundee.
14. Jim Forrest, against Morton.
15. Real Madrid.
16. Billy Ritchie.
17. Scottish Cup and League Cup.
18. Premier Championship and League Cup. Celtic were runners-up in both.
19. Aberdeen.
20. Celtic.
21. Aberdeen in both the Scottish Cup and League Cup.
22. Scottish Cup, against Airdrie.
23. Hibernian.
24. Aberdeen.
25. Six.

MISCELLANEOUS

1. Buffalo Bill.
2. Robert Fleck.
3. Barry Ferguson.
4. Neale Cooper.
5. Russell Latapy.
6. Three – John Greig, Sandy Jardine, Brian Laudrup.
7. Ian Ferguson.
8. Neil Murray.
9. 1988.
10. Eleven years.
11. Ally McCoist.
12. Mark Hateley in 1994.
13. Gerry Neef.
14. He first met his wife, who was an airline hostess on the flight.
15. Ayr United.
16. Jim Watt.
17. 1994.
18. Bobby Charlton, George Best and Peter Bonetti.
19. Lilac.
20. Fraser Wishart.
21. Lex Gold.
22. Manchester United.
23. Ian McMillan.

24. Davie Provan.
25. Bob Sutherland.

COMPENDIUM

1. Both played for Sunderland.
2. They all played in North America.
3. Charbonnier and Klos.
4. Alex MacDonald.
5. Davie Kirkwood.
6. Robert Prytz, with Malmo.
7. Paul Gascoigne.
8. 1987.
9. Allan Johnston.
10. Daniel Prodan.
11. 928.
12. Stanley Matthews, who served briefly at Ibrox in the war years.
13. Peter Huistra.
14. It was a Rangers International select.
15. Johan Cruyff.
16. They faced Rangers in the Ibrox International Tournament in 1984.

17. Rangers faced them all in season 1984–85.
18. 2–2.
19. Arsenal, Chelsea and Cardiff City.
20. In the John Greig Testimonial match in 1978.
21. Oleg Kuznetsov.
22. Ralph Brand.
23. They both scored hat-tricks.
24. Alex Ferguson.
25. 1998.

MULTIPLE CHOICE

1. John Greig.
2. Rangers.
3. Denmark.
4. 1977.
5. Eleven years.
6. Nineteen.
7. Five.
8. Princess Alexandra.
9. Twenty-eight.
10. 5ft 10in.
11. Forty-nine.

12. Fourteen, including one with Motherwell.
13. Twenty-seven.
14. Three (Jardine, Black, Clark).
15. Eric Caldow.
16. Derek Ferguson.
17. Robbie Williams.
18. 1971.
19. Dundee United, who took the Scottish Cup.
20. Six-a-side.
21. They all played in Vancouver, Canada.
22. Gordon Smith.
23. Partick Thistle.
24. Pele.
25. Arnold Palmer – he was once an Ibrox shareholder.

MIXED BAG

1. Peter McCloy.
2. Fiorentina.
3. Willie Johnston.
4. Stoke City, following the Rangers player's appearance in a testimonial match.
5. 1937.

6. Stanley Matthews.
7. Norrie Martin.
8. Sandy Jardine.
9. St Etienne.
10. Robert Russell.
11. Pittodrie.
12. Johnny Hubbard and Don Kichenbrand.
13. Gordon Ramsay.
14. Tom Sutherland.
15. Allan McLaren.
16. Joe Mason.
17. Dundee.
18. Jimmy Caskie.
19. Dumbarton.
20. Airdrie.
21. Jim Forrest.
22. Morton.
23. Thirty-eight.
24. Andy Penman.
25. Red Star Belgrade.

POT LUCK

1. Graeme Souness.
2. Two.
3. Watford.
4. Maurice Johnston.
5. 1989.
6. Twenty years.
7. McDiarmid Park.
8. Terry Hurlock, Mark Walters, and Mark Hateley.
9. Walter Smith.
10. The UEFA three-foreigner rule which limited the number of foreign players clubs could field in European competition.
11. David Robertson.
12. Dave McPherson and Ally Maxwell.
13. 1995–96.
14. Ray Wilkins at Queens Park Rangers.
15. Anorthosis Famagusta.
16. Forfar Athletic.
17. Valencia.
18. Clydebank.
19. Two – Ajax and Barcelona.
20. Max Murray.
21. Peter McCloy and Colin Stein.
22. Partisan Belgrade.

23. Burnley.
24. Hamilton Accies.
25. It was a gift from French side St Etienne.